LEARNING FOR LIFE & WORK

PERSONAL DEVELOPMENT

FOR CCEA GCSE

COLOURPOINT
EDUCATIONAL

Paula McCullough

ISBN: 978 1 906578 56 5

First Edition
First Impression

Layout and design: April Sky Design
Printed by: GPS Colour Graphics Ltd

COLOURPOINT
EDUCATIONAL

Colourpoint Books
Colourpoint House
Jubilee Business Park
Jubilee Road
Newtownards
County Down
Northern Ireland
BT23 4YH

Tel: 028 9182 6339
Fax: 028 9182 1900
E-mail: info@colourpoint.co.uk
Web site: www.colourpoint.co.uk

The Author

Paula McCullough has over 22 years experience of teaching in Northern Ireland and examining with CCEA. She is currently head of the Religious Education Department at Methodist College Belfast and also teaches LLW to GCSE level.

Acknowledgments

Special thanks go to the editor, Michael Spence, who has guided me through the whole writing process. Without him, this book would not have happened.

Thanks also to Colourpoint for giving me the opportunity to work on this series for LLW, and to Jill Armer at CCEA for her helpful support and guidance.

I would also like to thank my family for putting up with me when I became totally engrossed in writing.

For Frazer, Peter and Michael.

Picture credits

All photographs from iStock Photo with the following exceptions:

5 (right), 8 (left and top right), 14 (right and bottom left), 15 (all), 21 (bottom right), 25, 31 (bottom right), 42 (bottom), 46 (centre).

Michael Spence:	36 (right)
Rachel Irwin:	52 (left)
Peter McCullough:	57 (bottom right) and author photograph.

CONTENTS

Chapter one

MAXIMISING AND SUSTAINING HEALTH AND WELL-BEING

CHAPTER SUMMARY

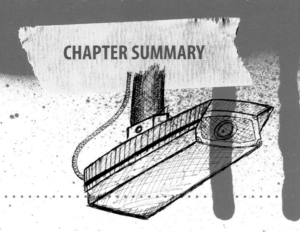

In this chapter you will be studying:

- What it means to be healthy.
- The benefits of following a healthy lifestyle.
- The importance of exercise and a healthy diet.
- The risks associated with substance abuse, including drugs, alcohol and cigarettes.

HEALTH

WHAT DOES IT MEAN TO BE HEALTHY?

There is more to being healthy than simply not feeling ill. A healthy person is at the peak of condition, will be around the right weight for their height, take regular exercise and have a balanced diet. Being healthy involves the whole person. It is a combination of feeling good physically, emotionally and socially. These three elements are often referred to as the 'Health Triangle'.

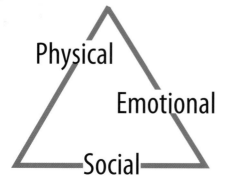

Most doctors say that healthy people live longer, happier and more successful lives – so good health is important!

DIFFERENT TYPES OF HEALTH

Physical health: Consider your body to be like a complex machine, where all the parts are operating correctly and efficiently, receiving the right type and amount of fuel. Everything is in good working order. However, we are more than just machines – other factors go towards a healthy human.

Social health: People are generally sociable – we need interaction with other humans for general well-being.

Having good relationships can give a person a more positive attitude to life. Relating socially with others is thought to release chemicals into the brain which can affect personality and general well-being.

Social health is also concerned with the environment a person lives in. Inadequate housing, over-crowded living conditions, a low income, work related stress and poor education can all have a negative impact on health.

Emotional health: Mental or emotional well-being gives a person the ability to lead a full life, confident that they will be able to cope when life's challenges come their way. People with positive emotional health are also good at helping others. At the other end of the scale, poor emotional health is when a person is feeling low and finding it hard to cope; they may also be feeling lonely and isolated.

Info Box

grow up in, the knowledge and skills and experience collected throughout life and how these are used."

Source: http://www.samaritans.org/your_emotional_health.aspx

FACTORS AFFECTING HEALTH

There are many factors influencing a person's health.

Physical health is often affected by illness, diet and exercise. However, a person's genetic make-up and the environment in which they live are also important. Conditions in housing, school and the workplace can have either a positive or negative impact on **social health**, too. Having to put up with poor facilities or a hostile environment can be damaging to health. There are many influences on a person's **emotional health**, such as loss of friendship, bereavement, unemployment, moving to a new school or family difficulties. Emotional health can be positively affected by a new friendship, joining a club or society or taking up a new skill.

Samaritans is a voluntary organisation providing emotional support for those who are experiencing feelings of distress and despair. This is what they say on their website about emotional health:

"Emotional health is about how balanced and confident we feel emotionally. If something happens and we feel low emotionally, getting back on track can be difficult. People do not automatically have either good or poor emotional health. Your emotional health depends on the circumstances you

There is a lot of positive action a person can take to try and improve their health. A person can take responsibility for themselves by eating a healthy diet and getting enough physical exercise.

Emotional health can be strengthened by:

- Talking about problems, fears and anxieties rather than bottling them up.
- Spending quality time with friends.
- Taking 'time out' for yourself.
- Avoiding alcohol and other drugs as a way of coping with pressure or dealing with stress.

NEWS ITEM

SOCIAL FACTORS KEY TO ILL HEALTH

Social factors – rather than genetics – are to blame for huge variations in ill health and life expectancy around the world, a report concludes.

The World Health Organization (WHO) has carried out a three-year analysis of the "social determinants" of health. The report concludes "social injustice is killing people on a grand scale". For instance, a boy living in the deprived Glasgow suburb of Calton will live on average 28 years less than a boy born in nearby affluent Lenzie. Similarly, the average life expectancy in London's wealthy Hampstead was 11 years longer than in nearby St Pancras. The research also shows that a girl in the African country of Lesotho is, on average, likely to live 42 years less than a girl in Japan.

In Sweden, the risk of a woman dying during pregnancy and childbirth is one in 17,400, but in Afghanistan the odds are one in eight. The report, drawn up by an eminent panel of experts forming the WHO's Commission on the Social Determinants of Health, found that, in almost all countries, poor socioeconomic circumstances equated to poor health. The differences were so marked that genetics and biology could not begin to explain them. The report highlights education, affordable housing, management of access to unhealthy foods and social security protection as key. It also said that governments should take action to ensure a living wage for workers, and working conditions that reduce work-related stress and ensure a healthy work-life balance.

Story taken from BBC NEWS August 2008.
Source: http://news.bbc.co.uk/1/hi/health/7584056.stm

6

ACTIVITIES

1. Read the news item. Prepare a two minute speech on what action could be taken to improve levels of social health.

2. Design a poster to help promote a healthy school environment. Remember to refer to physical, social and emotional health.

DISCUSSION

1. Discuss how each of the following may have a negative effect on a person's emotional health:
   - Loss of friendship
   - Bereavement
   - Loss of job
   - Moving school or house
   - Difficulties with parents or carers

2. Here are some factors which could have a positive effect on a person's emotional health:
   - Forming a new friendship
   - Developing a new skill

   What others can you think of?

CHECK YOUR LEARNING – HEALTH

1. What is meant by the 'Health Triangle'?
2. What actions can a person take to try and improve their overall health?
2. Explain what is meant by each of the following:
   • Physical health • Social health • Emotional health

DIET

WHAT IS MEANT BY A BALANCED DIET?

The food we eat can be divided into five main groups:

- Proteins, such as meat, fish eggs and beans.
- Fruit and vegetables.
- Carbohydrates, such as rice, pasta and bread.
- Milk and diary products.
- Foods containing fat and sugar.

In the UK, most people eat a diet containing too much fat, salt and sugar, but not enough wholegrains, fresh fruit and vegetables. A healthy diet is a balanced diet – there needs to be the right proportion of foods from each group. A sensible diet will include plenty of carbohydrates, fruit and vegetables, milk and dairy products, and enough protein, but will go easy on fatty and sugary items. Eating a variety of foods in the right proportion means that our bodies get all the nutrients needed for good health.

ACTIVITY

Plan a menu for a teenager for the next three days. Make sure you include all the food groups. Be sensible about junk food!

SPECIAL DIETS

Some people have to follow a special diet and eliminate or restrict certain foods, perhaps because of a health condition. Others choose not to eat particular types of food because of their beliefs. Two examples of this are vegetarians and vegans.

A vegetarian will avoid all products that come from killing an animal. This means they will not eat any meat, poultry or fish. Vegetarians will eat eggs and dairy products, such as milk, yoghurt and cheese.

A vegan will avoid all animal products. This means no meat of any kind, but also no eggs, honey or dairy products. Vegans will also avoid wearing products made from leather (such as shoes and belts) choosing a synthetic alternative instead.

Nowadays, most supermarkets stock organic foods. Organic food is farmed naturally without the use of potentially harmful chemicals, growth hormones or genetic modification. Some people try to base their diet entirely on organic produce as they are concerned about the use of artificial pesticides and fertilisers.

THE ADVANTAGES OF HEALTHY EATING

Some people might claim that eating a healthy diet is boring, too expensive or too much effort – it means giving up all their favourite foods. In fact, the advantages far outweigh the disadvantages both in the short and long term. A healthy diet can contribute to:

- Clear skin, strong hair and nails
- Being the correct weight and avoiding problems associated with obesity
- Feeling fit and full of energy
- Good levels of concentration and mental alertness
- Avoiding health problems, such as high blood pressure and cholesterol levels, heart disease and diabetes
- Living a long, healthy life.

FAST FOOD, CONVENIENCE FOOD AND JUNK FOOD

Achieving the right balance and eating a healthy diet can be difficult and often the pressures of modern living do not make it easy. After a busy day it can be tempting to go to the local takeaway **(fast food)** or grab a microwave meal from the supermarket shelf **(convenience food)**.

Eating these kinds of foods occasionally is not going to cause health problems. Some ready meals are additive-free and available as healthier options. However, many fast foods and convenience foods contain high levels of fat, sugar and salt, with not much fibre, vitamins or minerals. Many nutritionists would consider them to be 'junk food' as they have very little nutritional value. Snacks, such as crisps and sweets, would also be considered junk food.

JUNK FOOD

There are health implications in consuming large or regular quantities of fast food, convenience food or junk food:

Heart disease – This is due to high levels of fat and cholesterol clogging the arteries.

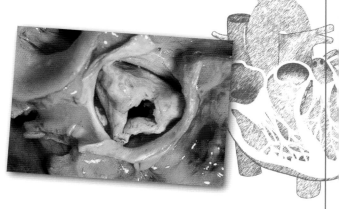

Poor concentration – Fatty fast foods take a lot of energy to digest. As a result the person feels drowsy and suffers reduced concentration.

Lack of energy – Junk foods get their name because they do not contain any nutrients which are beneficial to the human body.

Diabetes – Eating a lot of junk food can damage the pancreas, resulting in diabetes.

Liver failure – The high salt content of many convenience foods and snacks can damage the liver.

Obesity – Many fast food restaurants 'super size' their portions. This encourages over-eating.

DISCUSSION

"The fast food industry is booming – there's always a new chip shop or pizza delivery service starting up. It's what people want to eat, so it can't be all bad, can it?"

- Do you agree? How would you respond to this statement?

- Do you think that adverts for junk food ought to be banned? Explain your answer.

ACTIVITY

Keep a food diary for a week. In a small group, compare your results.
- Identify the five food groups.
- Identify the healthy and unhealthy parts of each person's diet.
- Suggest healthy alternatives.

OBESITY

Obesity is a medical condition, where a person has become so overweight that excess body fat is having a negative effect on their health.

A person's body mass index (BMI) is a measurement which relates weight to height. It is used by doctors as a way of indicating whether a person is obese. A BMI of between 18 and 25 would be considered healthy; between 25 and 30 indicates overweight but not obese, and over 30 is a sign of obesity.

ACTIVITY

Calculate your own BMI:
1. Measure how tall you are in metres.
2. Multiply this figure by itself.
3. Weigh yourself in kilograms.
4. Divide your weight by your height squared – the figure you get is your BMI

$$BMI = \frac{Weight\ (kg)}{Height^2\ (m)^2}$$

Alternatively, you can go online to a number of websites that will calculate this for you. Remember that BMI calculations are to be used as a guideline only and should not be taken too seriously.

There are a number of factors which can lead to obesity, the most common being lack of exercise and consuming more calories than the body needs. However, there are some medical conditions which can cause obesity. Some people believe there may be genetic reasons for obesity, although it could simply be that children learn eating and exercise habits from their parents.

Obesity is a serious issue, regarded by some health professionals as a major concern for the twenty-first century. Many people live a less active lifestyle than in the past and diets are now more likely to include high calorie snacks and fast foods.

Obesity is associated with the following risks:

- Heart disease
- High blood pressure
- Diabetes
- Some types of cancer

For children in particular there is the added risk of psychological problems such as depression and lack of self-esteem.

Tackling obesity requires a combination of diet and exercise. In some severe cases, obese people may be prescribed drugs to suppress their appetite or slow down the absorption of fat. If this is unsuccessful, then surgery may be carried out to reduce the size of the person's stomach and prevent over-eating. Education about healthy eating is also important, as it may help to prevent obesity in the first place or stop a person regaining any weight they have managed to lose.

ACTIVITIES

Use the Internet to research obesity.

- Find facts and figures for Northern Ireland.
- To what extent is obesity a major cause for concern in our society?
- What, if anything, do you think needs to be done to address the problem?

PROBLEMS WITH FOOD AND DIET

Some people may have problems maintaining a healthy, balanced diet, and develop an eating disorder. There are many reasons why food may become a problem for some people. These might include feelings of low self-esteem and a lack of confidence; problems with friends or family; bereavement or abuse. If a person is unhappy because they do not feel in control of their life, then they may start a rigid diet as this is one area that they can control. It is likely that many reasons combine to cause someone to have a problem with food.

evaluation

Evaluate the role of fast food in today's society.

What are the common eating disorders?

Anorexia – This eating disorder is characterised by very low body weight – the result of strict dieting almost to the point of starvation. A person suffering from anorexia will have a fear of gaining weight, even though they are very thin.

Bulimia – A person with bulimia may appear to be about the right weight. Bulimia involves periods of binge eating, followed by vomiting or misuse of laxatives.

Some sufferers may be both anorexic and bulimic, keeping to a rigid diet most of the time, but with occasional bouts of uncontrollable bingeing.

Many people may try and hide their eating disorder, but it is thought that around 1 in 100 teenage girls suffers from anorexia or bulimia, while 1 in 500 young men are affected.

Eating disorders are a very serious health issue, causing poor skin, hair and teeth; weakness and inability to concentrate; low self-esteem and a poor self-image. Many sufferers see themselves as 'too fat' when in fact they are dangerously thin. At their most extreme, eating disorders can result in death and a sufferer needs expert counselling to help them.

1. Explain what is meant by a 'balanced diet'.
2. What is the difference between a vegetarian diet and a vegan diet?
3. Outline a sensible approach to 'junk' food.
4. What are the health risks associated with being obese?

EXERCISE

WHY ARE THERE CONCERNS ABOUT EXERCISE?

We are becoming a nation of couch potatoes!

Even though there has been a massive growth in the number of fitness clubs and gyms, the fact is that many people today do not get enough physical exercise. It is not that people are becoming lazy; in fact, one of the reasons why people do not take enough exercise is that they are too busy with other activities. Demanding jobs and busy lifestyles often mean that a car or public transport is used, rather than healthier alternatives such as walking or cycling. Many of the occupations people have nowadays involve very little physical effort. The use of labour-saving machines in the home has made housework less of a physical chore than it was for previous generations. Technology may have made our lives easier, but we are less likely to be physically active.

CHILDREN AND YOUNG PEOPLE

Changing trends in lifestyle are having a huge impact on children and young people. The most popular leisure activities are those which involve doing something in front of a screen – using the computer, watching TV and DVDs, playing video games – all of which involve very little exercise. There needs to be a balance between screen time and physical activity.

Sadly, because of fear of violence, it is often not safe for young people to choose walking home as a healthy option. Parents and carers prefer to collect children in the car and know they have arrived home safely.

ACTIVITIES

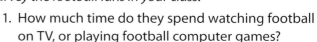

Survey the football fans in your class.

1. How much time do they spend watching football on TV, or playing football computer games?
2. How does this compare to the time spent actually playing football?

School age children will have PE and Games on their timetable. However, this is not enough physical activity for good health. Young people need around one hour of exercise each day. This does not need to be taken all at once; in fact it is better in sessions of around 10–15 minutes. Active play and sport are great ways to get exercise, so it need not be boring. Going to an aerobics or martial arts class with a couple of friends can

be an opportunity to socialise as well as get some exercise. Joining a team or taking up swimming or running might appeal to a competitive person. Regular exercise is essential for a healthy lifestyle.

What are the main ways you exercise?

- Keep a diary for a week and include all exercise that you do. For example, walking to school, PE classes, swimming club.
- How much time do you spend on physical activity each day?
- How does this compare with others in your group?
- Do you think you get enough exercise?

PHYSICAL FITNESS

An effective exercise session is one that will involve aerobic or cardiovascular exercise with bending and stretching. It is important to get out of breath and get the heart pumping (but don't overdo it!), and to build up suppleness in muscles and joints.

> There are three main elements to physical fitness:
>
> - **Stamina:** This means having a slow, powerful heartbeat and the ability to keep going for a long time without gasping for breath.
>
> - **Strength:** This comes from having well-toned muscles through regular exercise.
>
> - **Suppleness:** This means having flexibility in key areas of the body, such as neck, spine and joints.

THE POSITIVES – THE BENEFITS OF EXERCISE…

Regular exercise plays an important contribution to both physical and mental good health and can help towards:

- maintaining a healthy weight;
- an improved body shape;
- a reduction in stress level – exercise releases chemicals called endorphins into the bloodstream and these create feelings of well-being;
- an increase in energy level;
- improved brain function and mental awareness;
- improved health – exercise stimulates the body's own repair and defence mechanism;

- stronger bones and muscles with better ability to withstand injury;
- improved balance, strength and mobility;
- more social opportunities;
- a sense of achievement.

In the longer term, regular exercise can lead to greater independence as a person gets older. Muscles, bones and joints stay younger for longer through exercise. Regular exercise also means avoiding some serious health problems.

AND THE NEGATIVES – WHAT HAPPENS IF YOU DON'T

A person who does not get enough physical exercise can suffer in the short-term from:

- breathlessness;
- low energy levels;
- a flabby body;
- being overweight;
- stiff joints and poor posture.

The long-term effects of insufficient exercise are more serious and can include:

- heart disease;
- strokes;
- diabetes;
- osteoporosis;
- high blood pressure.

THE IMPORTANCE OF SLEEP

Are you getting enough sleep? It is important to balance physical activity with sufficient good quality rest to be at the peak of well-being.

Sleep is important for both physical and mental functioning and wellbeing. Previous studies suggest that people who do not get enough sleep are more likely to be overweight or obese. UK scientists found sleep deprivation led to hormonal changes which told the body to eat sugary or starchy food to provide an energy boost. But sleep problems can be a symptom of many other conditions, from problems with the thyroid gland to depression.

Source: http://news.bbc.co.uk/1/hi/6962085.stm

NEWS ITEM

JUNK SLEEP 'DAMAGING TEEN HEALTH'

Too many teenagers are damaging their health by not getting enough sleep and by falling asleep with electrical gadgets on, researchers say.

A third of 12 to 16-year-olds asked slept for between four to seven hours a night. Experts recommend eight hours. The Sleep Council, which conducted the poll of 1,000 teenagers, says gadgets in bedrooms such as computers and TVs are fuelling poor quality "junk sleep". Youngsters need to be taught that sleep is important for their health, it said. Almost a quarter of the teens surveyed admitted they fell asleep watching TV, listening to music or with other equipment still running, more than once a week. Nearly all had either a phone, music system or TV in their bedroom, and two thirds had all three. Among 12 to 14-year-old boys, nearly three in five (58%) had a phone, music player, TV and games console in their bedroom. While 40% of the teens said they were often tired during the day, just 10% placed much importance on getting a good night's sleep.

ACTIVITIES

Read the news item.

- Discuss in pairs whether you think it applies to you.
- Design a poster for 12-16-year-olds explaining the importance of a good night's sleep.

CHECK YOUR LEARNING – EXERCISE

1. What are the three main elements to physical fitness?
2. Suggest some easy ways for an inactive person to increase their level of physical activity.
3. Apart from health benefits, what other advantages are there to being physically active?

SUBSTANCE ABUSE

WHAT IS SUBSTANCE ABUSE?

Substance abuse can involve the following:
Taking an illegal drug (for example, heroin or cannabis).

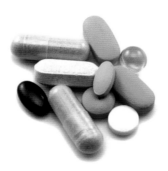

Taking a prescription drug that has not been prescribed for you by a doctor (for example, tranquilisers).

Using a legal substance that is addictive and potentially dangerous (for example, alcohol and nicotine).

Using a solvent or volatile substance for the effect it has on the body, not the use for which it was manufactured (for example, glue and lighter fuel).

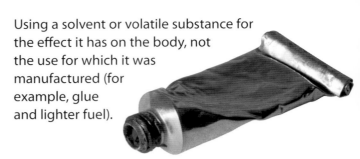

WHAT IS A DRUG?

The term 'drug' can be used to refer to any of the substances above.

A drug is a chemical (sometimes a poison) that acts on the central nervous system when taken into the body by being swallowed, injected, smoked or sniffed. These chemicals then interfere with the functioning of the brain.

Neurotransmitters enable the brain to send and receive messages throughout the body; however, drugs can block or enhance the effect of a neurotransmitter. This means that drugs can alter a person's mood and state of mind; affect vision, coordination and speech; create hallucinations or cause unconsciousness and death.

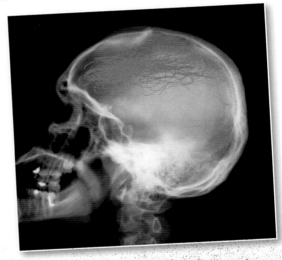

HOW ARE DRUGS CLASSIFIED?

Drugs can be classified according to how they affect the mind and body. There are 4 main groups:

Stimulants: These drugs cause the body to be stimulated, or speed up. A person using a stimulant drug may appear to be very lively, talkative and energetic, but this can quickly turn to agitation and aggression. Ecstasy and cocaine are stimulants.

Depressants: These drugs depress the nervous system and cause feelings of sleepiness and relaxation. A person using depressants may have slurred speech and uncoordinated movements, or may even slip into unconsciousness. Cannabis and alcohol are depressants.

Hallucinogens: These drugs create hallucinations where the user will 'trip' seeing odd shapes and colours or perhaps hear strange sounds. Trips can be either pleasant or terrifying; there is no guarantee how a hallucinogen will affect the body. However, if a person is feeling tense or unhappy before taking a hallucinogenic drug, the result will probably be unpleasant as they tend to magnify whatever mood you are in. LSD is a hallucinogen; ecstasy and cannabis also have hallucinogenic effects.

Opiates: These drugs can have a medical use in controlling severe pain. When abused they have the effect of blocking out feelings and making the user appear cut off from the world. Heroin is an opiate.

Info Box

THE LAW AND DRUGS

Illegal drugs can also be classified according to how dangerous they are, as this affects the legal penalties for having them in your possession or supplying them to others. At the time of writing, there are three categories:

CLASS A: These are considered to be the most harmful.
Examples: Ecstasy, LSD, heroin, cocaine, crack.
Penalty for possession: Up to 7 years in prison, an unlimited fine or both.
Penalty for dealing: Up to life imprisonment, an unlimited fine or both.

CLASS B: These are considered not as dangerous, unless they are injected (if this is the case, then they receive the Class A penalties).
Examples: Amphetamines, pholcodine.
Penalty for possession: Up to 5 years in prison, an unlimited fine or both.

Penalty for dealing: Up to 14 years in prison, an unlimited fine or both.

CLASS C: These are considered to be less harmful than other illegal drugs.
Examples: Cannabis, tranquilisers.
Penalties for possession: Up to 2 years in prison, an unlimited fine or both.
Penalties for dealing: Up to 14 years in prison, an unlimited fine or both.

(Sometimes laws relating to drug classification are updated. The laws listed here are the case as of the date of printing in 2010.)

THE LAW AND ALCOHOL

It is against the law for a young person under the age of 18 to:

- Buy alcoholic drink in a shop or bar;
- Ask someone else to buy it for them (even if this person is over 18);
- To pretend to be 18 and drink alcohol in a public place;

Police can confiscate alcoholic drink from a person under the age of 18, even if they say they are not drinking it but looking after it for someone else. However, a young person between the ages of 14 and 18 years is allowed to drink alcohol at home, with parental permission.

Alcohol laws vary from country to country. In America, for example, a person has to be over 21 years of age before they can legally buy alcoholic drink.

WHAT DOES IT MEAN TO BE ADDICTED TO DRUGS?

Drugs are addictive. This means the body quickly becomes used to them, so more and more have to be taken to achieve the same effect. When a person is addicted, it means they have a compulsion to keep taking or using something even though they know it is bad for their health. Addiction can be either physical or psychological.

Physical addiction is when a person's body becomes dependent on a drug in order to function properly. After a certain number of doses of the drug, your body will actually need to have the drug, or else you will suffer from withdrawal symptoms – sweating, dizziness, stomach cramps, alternating feelings of hot and cold, vomiting and diarrhoea. Heroin causes physical addiction.

Psychological addiction is when a person's mind becomes dependent on a drug. Cannabis, solvents and ecstasy are drugs which cause this kind of dependence. If you were to take them for a while, and then stop, your body would continue to function normally. However, you would crave the good feelings that the drug artificially and temporarily creates.

When a person becomes addicted to drugs, including alcohol, their behaviour will probably change. A conscientious student may start to ignore schoolwork or fail exams and drop out of clubs and sporting activities. Someone with a friendly, easy-going personality may start to be secretive or aggressive, or family members may notice that cash is missing as an addict needs more and more money to fund their habit.

WHY DO SOME YOUNG PEOPLE USE DRUGS AND ALCOHOL?

Here are some possible reasons:

For pleasure: The initial effects of taking certain drugs can be exhilarating and exciting. The problem is that these feelings and sensations do not last.

To fit in: Taking drugs can help people to be more sociable; inhibitions are removed and people feel more at ease in dealing with others.

Peer Pressure: A person may be persuaded by friends to start experimenting with drugs.

Stress: Some people find it hard to cope with the pressures of work or school and feel they need something to prevent feelings of anxiety. The breakdown of a relationship may also be a particularly difficult time.

Curiosity: If everyone seems to be talking about drugs and alcohol, or using them, this may tempt someone to try for themselves.

Availability: Illegal drugs are much more readily available than in the past, and many young people today have the money to spend on them.

Lifestyle: Some leisure activities, such as clubbing, often go hand in hand with taking drugs.

The example of celebrities: Some popular and admired celebrities do not set a good example when it comes to drugs and alcohol and they can be poor role models for impressionable young people.

ACTIVITY

Why do you think young people use alcohol and other drugs? Make a list of reasons.

CHOOSING NOT TO DRINK ALCOHOL

You might get the impression from the media that most young people like to abuse alcohol, given the opportunity! It is true that under-age drinking has become a very serious issue. However, many young people choose not to drink at all. This could be for religious reasons, or because they are aware of some of the dangers associated with drinking alcohol early in life, or simply because they do not like it! Making a positive decision not to drink alcohol is sometimes known as **abstinence.**

THE NEGATIVE EFFECTS OF USING DRUGS

The consequences of experimenting with drugs can be very serious, not just for the person involved but those around them as well. Here are some examples:

Financial difficulties: It can cost a lot of money to sustain an addiction, and often people who do have an addiction problem find it difficult to hold down a job. Many addicts live in poverty as all their money is spent on drugs; others turn to crime to feed their habit.

Trouble with the authorities: A student may be suspended from school if they are suspected of possessing drugs or distributing drugs to fellow pupils. In some cases the police may be involved. Although alcohol is a legal drug in society, it is not legal for a person under the age of 18.

Risk of injury: People under the influence of drugs or alcohol can lose control and this causes them to take foolish risks that they would not otherwise take. A person who drives after drinking alcohol is particularly likely to harm themselves and others.

Health problems: There are many health problems associated with drug abuse. Drug dependency can lead to mental illness; cannabis has been linked to schizophrenia and is even more damaging to the lungs than smoking cigarettes. Cocaine and amphetamines have been linked to heart problems,

while ecstasy can cause liver failure and panic attacks. The life expectancy of a person who abuses drugs is significantly reduced.

Illegal drugs do not come with dosage instructions and there are no guarantees as to their purity. As a result, it is easy to overdose unintentionally. In the UK, illegal drugs are the cause of around 1,400 deaths each year.

Damage to relationships: Addiction to drugs quickly tends to ruin personal relationships, as a person's character can change completely.

Alcoholism also breaks up many marriages. Family life can be seriously damaged, particularly if one or more members of the family are drug addicts.

Issues for young people: If a person's body is still growing and developing, then introducing harmful substances can have long-term consequences. A young person is more likely to suffer liver damage from heavy drinking than an older person.

Problems for society: Millions of pounds of public money are spent each year on health care for patients with alcohol or smoking related diseases. Surely this money could be put to better use? Another consideration is that a person dependant on an addictive substance is unlikely to be able to contribute fully to society.

SMOKING

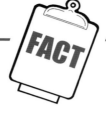

Did you know…

- Nicotine, the drug contained in tobacco, is highly addictive;

- Smoking causes harm to the environment – 40% of street litter is made up of cigarette butts;

- Smoking causes harm to other people through passive smoking;

- Smoking has been banned in all public places in Northern Ireland since April 2007, as it is so dangerous and unpleasant to others;

- Nicotine kills more people than any other drug (in 2005 there were over 100,000 deaths due to smoking in the UK);

- A woman who smokes while pregnant can cause her baby to have a low birth weight and breathing difficulties;

- Smokers' babies are more at risk of cot death;

- Smoking is very damaging to health, causing cancer of the mouth, throat and lungs, emphysema – a chronic lung condition, and damage to the heart.

- Smoking can cause skin damage, especially to the face, as a smoker is constantly in a cloud of poisonous fumes;

- Smokers have bad breath and discoloured teeth and nails, as the chemicals in nicotine cause them to become yellow;

- The younger a person is when they start smoking, the more likely they are to die a premature death;

- A cigarette contains over 4,000 chemicals, at least 10% of which are carcinogenic (cancer causing), such as:

    – Ammonia (found in cleaning products)

    – Arsenic (found in rat poison)

    – Nitro benzene (a chemical added to petrol)

    – Acetone (an ingredient in nail polish remover)

ALCOHOL

Did you know…

- Alcohol is a highly addictive and dangerous drug;

- Alcohol is a poison, with the same chemical make-up as a general anaesthetic;

- Drinking alcohol can reduce vital brain development in young people;

- Young people who start drinking in their early teens are more likely to develop a problem with alcohol in later life;

- Young people who drink are more likely to be involved in crime as it can give a false sense of courage and make a person more likely to take risks;

- Alcohol also causes an increase in aggression and people who drink too much are more likely to be involved in assaults resulting in injury to themselves or others;

- Drinking alcohol can make a person more likely to end up in hospital as the result of an accident, as it causes a lack of co-ordination and slows down reaction times;

- Alcohol can lead to physical health problems, including serious damage to the liver, stomach and heart;

- Drinking too much alcohol can lead to mental health problems, such as depression and paranoia;

- Drinking alcohol can lead to risky sexual behaviour, as it lowers inhibitions. This can result in an unplanned pregnancy or sexually transmitted infection (STI);

- If a woman drinks alcohol while pregnant, the unborn baby can be permanently damaged;

- Alcohol causes more social harm than all other drugs put together, through its negative effect on families and marriages;

- In Northern Ireland, alcohol-related accidents and incidents cost over £700 million per year.

HELP AND SUPPORT FOR PEOPLE WITH ADDICTION PROBLEMS

It is widely recognised today that substance abuse and addiction are serious problems for society and affect many people. As a result there is a range of help available, including health professionals, self-help groups and voluntary organisations.

Carlisle House is a residential treatment centre, aiming to help those affected by substance abuse. Their work is described in more detail on their website:

"Carlisle House is a residential substance misuse treatment centre situated near the centre of Belfast. It caters for individuals 18–65 years old, from the greater Belfast area and North Antrim. Carlisle House also welcomes private clients. It offers a range of services, advice and information, treatment programmes, and ongoing support services. Carlisle House was established in 1992 by the Board of Social Witness of the Presbyterian Church in Ireland and is a registered charity."

Source: http://www.carlislehouse.org/whoweare/index.php

Carlisle House offers a residential programme of four to eight weeks duration. It requires a commitment to change, and a willingness to enter the process of honesty, openness and self-exploration. There is mutual agreement between the staff at Carlisle House and the person seeking help as to the best course of treatment.

NICAS

The Northern Ireland Community Addiction Service (NICAS) is one of the main charities in Northern Ireland dedicated to helping people who are addicted to drugs and alcohol. They have centres in Belfast and treat people from all over Northern Ireland.

The following information is taken from their website:

"The Northern Ireland Community Addiction Service (NICAS) is a registered charity providing treatment and support for people who are dependent on alcohol or drugs. We provide tailor-made treatment programmes for people with drug or alcohol problems, delivered in community settings. We also give confidential support for people affected by someone else's drinking or drug use.

Around half of NICAS clients are referred by GPs, social workers and other health and social care professionals.

Alcohol or drug use can cause problems in the workplace. Employee performance and morale can be affected by alcohol or drug dependency. It has been estimated that alcohol misuse alone costs industry in Northern Ireland £238 million in lost productivity."

Source: http://nicas.info/info/

NICAS offers help to employers, so they can help workers who might be facing problems with addiction. This includes drug and alcohol awareness training and individual treatment programmes for employees who are dependant on alcohol or drugs.

evaluation

Evaluate different strategies that could be used to reduce the abuse of drugs and alcohol by young people.

Public Health Agency

The Public Health Agency for Northern Ireland is an organisation run by the government. They aim to raise public awareness through their posters and publications. These cover a wide range of health-related topics, such as drugs, alcohol, nutrition and mental health. There are designed to have maximum impact in schools, workplaces and public areas outdoors. You may have noticed some of their posters on bus shelters or billboards.

HOW SCHOOLS COULD HELP

Learning to live a healthy lifestyle can contribute to a person's physical, social and emotional well-being. A balanced diet, regular exercise, a sensible attitude to addictive substances and time for leisure and social interaction will help a person make the most of life: education, work and free time.

Schools can play a vital role in helping and encouraging students to have a healthy lifestyle and achieve optimum physical and mental health. Schools can do this through:

The school curriculum: This can be developed to support a healthy lifestyle, with a variety of subjects contributing to lessons on diet, nutrition, exercise and substance abuse. It is also important for students to

have sports and PE on their timetables, to encourage physical activity and teamwork.

A healthy eating policy: Vending machines should not dispense fizzy drinks, crisps or sweets, but water, fresh juice or healthy snacks. Drinking water should be freely available. The school cafeteria should provide a choice of nutritious, fresh food.

Pastoral care: Specially trained teachers, working alongside counsellors, should be equipped to help and advise students about emotional issues.

Promoting cycling or walking to school: Bicycle sheds and changing facilities could be provided by the school, along with luminous armbands to ensure students' safety when cycling or walking to school.

An effective anti-bullying policy: It is important for students to feel safe and unthreatened in their school environment. Being bullied at school could have a detrimental effect on a person's emotional health.

ACTIVITIES

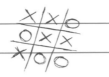

Work in groups of about 4:

- A school is concerned about reports that many young people eat an unhealthy diet and do not get enough exercise. Create a school policy to help promote a healthier lifestyle for pupils.

- Make a list of the ways in which your school encourages pupils to make healthy choices. Suggest ways in which your school could do more to encourage good health.

SOME CONTROVERSIAL ISSUES

- Is the ban on smoking in public places a positive move to a healthier society, or do you think it infringes on the rights of smokers?

- Supermarkets often have 'special offers' on alcoholic drink; some bars and clubs have a 'happy hour' when drinks are cheap. Are these wrong because it is encouraging people to drink too much?

- Some people argue that alcohol is more harmful than cannabis, so why should cannabis be illegal? The police could concentrate on more important matters if they did not have to deal with a large number of cannabis users.

- If alcohol is more harmful than cannabis, why should alcohol be legal?

- Should people be treated on the NHS if their condition is the result of alcoholism or drug abuse? Surely their condition is their own fault and they cannot expect their treatment to be paid for out of public money.

ACTIVITIES

Choose one of the issues from the list above.

- Use it as the basis for a class debate,

  or

- Write a letter to a newspaper explaining your view.

CHECK YOUR LEARNING – DRUGS

1. What is solvent abuse?

2. What is a drug?

3. Explain the different ways that drugs affect the body. Give examples.

4. What is the difference between physical addiction and psychological addiction?

5. What are the risks to health associated with:
   – alcohol – smoking – illegal drugs?
   Write a short paragraph for each.

6. Explain why some young people might be tempted to take drugs.

ACTIVITY

Use the Internet to research:
Find out more about the help available for people affected by substance abuse, from both professional organisations and voluntary groups.

EXTENSION TASK

Choose one of the aspects of living a healthy lifestyle covered in this chapter.

Produce a PowerPoint presentation that could be shown to the rest of your class.

FACTS ABOUT ILLEGAL DRUGS

These are the most commonly used illegal drugs, arranged in order, with cannabis being the most widely used.

DRUG	STREET NAME	APPEARANCE	HOW IT IS TAKEN	EFFECTS	DANGERS
CANNABIS/ MARIJUANA	Dope Weed Grass	Cannabis – a lump of brown resin; Marijuana – dried leaves	Usually rolled into a joint and smoked; sometimes eaten	Feelings of relaxation; sometimes causes hallucinations	Mental health problems; has an aging effect on the brain; long-term use can cause lack of motivation and paranoia; physical problems include lung disease and cancer
COCAINE	Coke Snow Charlie Crack	White powder; Crack cocaine comes as small crystals	Cocaine in powder form is sniffed; crack is heated and smoked	At first, the user is lively, confident and talkative; this quickly changes to feelings of agitation and depression	Highly addictive, especially if smoked as crack cocaine. Can cause fits, convulsions and panic attacks; can lead to mental health problems
ECSTASY	E Pills XTC Hug drug	Tablets of various shapes and colours	Swallowed	Some users feel happy, lively and friendly; others feel anxious and scared	Can cause panic attacks; also associated with liver, kidney and heart problems; increases body temperature and can lead to dehydration
LSD	Acid Tabs Microdots	Colourless liquid on a tiny stamp, usually with a picture on it.	The paper square is eaten or sucked	Weird hallucinations which can be pleasant or terrifying; these can last for hours	Temporary brain disturbance can cause users to behave dangerously; the hallucinations can be repeated as 'flashbacks' weeks later
AMPHETAMINES	Speed Whiz Uppers	Tablets or capsules	Swallowed or ground to a powder and injected	Users feel as if they have lots of energy and may talk non-stop; can quickly change to depression	Can cause severe psychological problems; difficulty with normal sleep patterns; can be fatal if taken with other drugs or alcohol
HEROIN	Smack H Junk	White powder	Usually injected; sometimes smoked	Users feel sleepy, relaxed and cut off from the world; totally unconcerned about anything	The most addictive illegal drug; easy to overdose; sharing needles can lead to HIV or hepatitis; addicts totally neglect their physical health

EXAM FOCUS

This section will appear at the end of every chapter. It will help you to develop your exam skills.

As well as covering different topics, your exam will have different types of question to test different skills. One of these skills is to demonstrate your knowledge and understanding.

The following question tests this skill:

(a) Name two illegal drugs.

[2 marks]

(b) Identify and explain two ways in which a young person's health and well-being can be supported by their school.

[4 marks]

(c) Identify and explain two ways in which exercise can improve a person's health.

[4 marks]

Question taken from CCEA's GCSE LLW Modular Specimen Assessment Materials for first teaching September 2009

When answering part (b) and part (c) of this question, start by clearly stating what you are going to write about, then give your explanation.

You could begin part (b) in the following way:

'Healthy eating policy – the school vending machines should not provide unhealthy snacks and fizzy drinks. Healthy food such as fruit and salad should be on the menu in the canteen, with fresh drinking water freely available.'

Continue this answer adding an example of your own.

Chapter two
CONCEPT OF SELF

CHAPTER SUMMARY

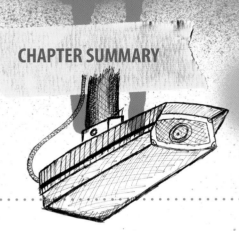

In this chapter you will be studying:

- How to identify your personal strengths and weaknesses.

- What is meant by self-confidence, self-esteem and self-worth.

- Setting targets and working towards goals.

- Pressures on young people.

- Strategies to cope with these pressures.

WHAT IS 'CONCEPT OF SELF'?

This topic is about you as a person and what it is that makes you unique. Everyone has their own particular talents and abilities, as well as weaknesses. What are yours?

Each person has a mental picture of themselves, or self-image, with a mix of both positive and negative ideas.

ME

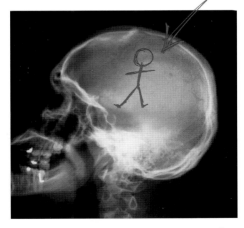

Everybody can make a positive contribution to their home, school, workplace, and society. Your contribution may not be the same as someone else's – but that does not mean it is any less valuable. Life would be very boring if everyone was exactly the same.

PERSONAL STRENGTHS & WEAKNESSES

SELF-CONFIDENCE, SELF-ESTEEM AND SELF-WORTH

These terms refer to the feelings you have about yourself, and they can be either positive or negative.

Self-confidence: This refers to your own opinion about your talents and abilities. A person who believes that they can generally complete tasks well most of the time, would have high self-confidence.

On the other hand, a person who often feels very negative about their abilities could be said to have low self-confidence. People who lack self-confidence might feel nervous or unsure when doing something new, or perhaps worry that people will laugh at them. Many people have high self-confidence in some areas but feel unsure in others, depending on where their particular strengths and weaknesses lie. This is perfectly healthy. However, no one should have such a low opinion of themselves that they think they are useless at everything, or that anything they try will end in failure.

25

Self-esteem: This refers to your personal feelings about yourself. If you are generally happy with who you are as a person, you could be described as having high self-esteem.

People with low self-esteem find it difficult to accept praise for doing something well; yet when something goes wrong, they tend to think that it is all their fault. People with high self-esteem can generally cope better with difficulties: they can acknowledge that there is a problem, then take action to tackle it. People with low self-esteem tend to be critical and hard on themselves, rather than finding ways to cope.

Having continually low self-esteem can be very damaging. A person's attitude towards themselves affects their attitude towards others. If you feel good about yourself most of the time then it is easier to be positive to those around you. On the other hand, people with low self-esteem sometimes feel they have to bully other people or put them down in order to feel good about themselves.

Self-worth: This refers to how you rate your value as a person in your relationships with others. A person with low self-worth may often feel left out and unpopular, or that friends are deliberately trying to exclude them. They may often have feelings of jealousy and in a sexual relationship they may accuse their partner of being unfaithful. It is as if they feel that they are not worthy of having a friendship or close relationship with another person. Recognising your own self-worth is also an important step in recognising the worth of others.

ACTIVITY

Take a few minutes to rate your own self-confidence, self-esteem and self-worth out of ten.

Do you think they change from day to day?

Why do you think this is?

WHAT FACTORS CAN HAVE AN INFLUENCE?

There are a number of factors that can have an influence on a person's self-confidence, self-esteem and self-worth. Some influences could be:

Success at school: This could be academic success, playing for a school team, achieving in music or drama, being voted onto the school council – there are many possibilities! Feeling successful in just one aspect of school life can help improve self-confidence.

Peer group: Having a circle of friends who enjoy your company and will support you can have a very positive effect on self-esteem and self-worth. On the other hand, poor relationships can lead to feelings of low self-worth.

Family: Most parents and carers will do their best to support and encourage their child. Children have to be taught correct behaviour, and parents and family play a key role in this. However, criticism should be constructive, with the intention of helping a young person improve themselves and avoid future mistakes. Criticism should not result in a child feeling useless or unloved as this can lower self-esteem. Knowing that you are valued by your family can give a sense of self-worth.

Physical appearance: Very few people are totally happy with their looks. Most people would change something about their appearance if given the chance, such as hair, skin, body shape, weight or height. However, it is especially common for young people, going through the changes of adolescence, to feel very unhappy about their looks. This may be made even worse if a person is bullied because of their appearance.

There is direct link between looking good and feeling good - and the person who is generally content with their appearance is more likely to have higher self-confidence. Some young people may feel so negative about themselves that they develop an eating disorder, which can be very dangerous.

Race and religion: Membership of a racial or religious cultural group, can give people a sense of belonging to a wider family. Religious beliefs can shape how a person sees themselves in relation to the rest of the world. Sadly, some people in society are prejudiced towards those who are of a different race to them or hold religious views which they do not share; they might think that this justifies inferior treatment.

At school, children may be subjected to bullying directed towards their religious or ethnic background. To be on the receiving end of prejudice and discrimination may affect a person's feelings of self-confidence and self-esteem.

Sexuality: Sexual attraction and relationships can have a huge effect on people's self-confidence, self-esteem and self-worth. Break-ups can sometimes have a negative effect on how people feel about themselves, and it can be important to keep relationships in perspective.

Some people may find themselves the victim of prejudice and discrimination because of their sexual orientation. This may be particularly distressing for a young person struggling to come to terms with their sexuality. To be subjected to unkind remarks from other young people can lead to lowered self-esteem and self-worth.

Learning difficulties: Some people may have low self-confidence or self-esteem because of insensitivity from others regarding a learning difficulty. It is worth remembering that many people are diagnosed with learning difficulties; two of the most common, dyslexia and dyscalculia, are not related to a person's intelligence.

DYSLEXIA – Dyslexia comes from the Greek language and means 'difficulty with words'. The right side of the brain controls artistic skills, while the left side controls logic and maths skills. People with dyslexia have a slightly more developed right side of the brain, making them very creative, but also giving problems with reading and spelling.

DYSCALCULIA – Many students experience difficulties with maths, but this does not mean they have dyscalculia. A person with dyscalculia has difficulty with numbers and this may include telling the time, calculating prices, handling change or playing games that require keeping track of scores.

HOW TO HELP YOURSELF

We often have very little control over the way we are treated by others. However, a person can still have a very significant influence on their own levels of self-confidence, self-esteem and self-worth. Here are some suggestions:

Positive thinking: This is more than just thinking the right thoughts; it is about a person's whole approach to life. In most situations there will good points and bad, but it is important to focus more on the positives than the negatives. Positive thinking also involves thinking well of yourself, not being too critical or putting yourself down. It also means dealing with other people in a positive way.

Believe in yourself: If you really believe that you can achieve something, and you are prepared to make an effort, then you will probably enjoy some success. On the other hand, being negative and unwilling to try is far more likely to end in failure, and often leads to more negative feelings.

Be realistic: It is great to aim high and set yourself a challenge, but make sure you are not expecting too much of yourself. Don't compare yourself to other people who may find a particular task easier than you.

Look on the bright side: It is important to keep a sense of perspective. Even if a situation is really dreadful, try not to be overwhelmed by negative feelings or thinking that it is entirely your fault. Try to have a balanced approach, and look for an opportunity to learn from the experience.

PERSONALITY TYPES

Each person is a unique individual, with their own personality. However, many psychologists would say that there are sixteen main personality types, according to whether a person would be more inclined to:

- Be either an extrovert or an introvert;
- Use either their senses or their intuition;
- Make decisions based on either thoughts or feelings;
- Use either their judgment in a situation or their perception.

An **extrovert** is a person who would be outgoing, sociable and talkative, even with strangers; an **introvert** is quieter, preferring to be with a small group of friends rather than a large crowd.

A person who uses their **senses** notices what is going on around them, while a person who uses **intuition** sees the 'big picture' and can realise future implications for a current action.

A person who makes decisions based on **thoughts** will take the most logical course of action, whether they like it or not; a person who uses their **feelings** will decide how to act according to each situation.

People who rely on their **judgement** will make lists of things to do and schedule things in advance; those who rely on **perception** will act spontaneously and do things at the last minute, rather than planning ahead.

Work in pairs

- Discuss with your partner which personality traits best apply to you. Do you agree with your partner's assessment of your character?

STRENGTHS AND WEAKNESSES

Different personality types have their own particular strengths and potential weaknesses. For example, an extrovert may be very sociable and entertaining, but on the other hand may talk too much and dominate a conversation. The person who can work independently and plan ahead on a project may have difficulties working with others. The person who thinks everything through carefully to reach the right course of action may be too rigid at times. The diplomatic person, always aware of the feelings of others, may not be assertive enough on some occasions.

People have different skills and abilities – some are musical, others good at sport; you could be an intellectual, or good at solving practical problems; some people have a natural ability to be caring; others to be organised and efficient.

Each person has their own strengths and weaknesses; whilst no-one is perfect, no-one should feel completely negative about themselves, either. Everyone has their own contribution to make to the world they live in and the people they interact with.

Think about your own personality.
Draw two columns on a sheet of paper and label them 'strengths' and 'weaknesses'.
Here are some ideas to think about. Decide which apply to you and add points of your own.

My personal strengths…
I am a loyal friend
I have an easy-going personality
I can cope with failure and try to learn from my mistakes
I like to work as part of a team
I can work independently

I am well organised
I am patient with other people
I work hard at school
I help out a lot at home
I believe I can do well if I try hard

My weaknesses…
I get impatient if people do not see my point of view
I can be very forgetful
I am often late
I get too upset if others annoy me
I can be bossy
I talk too much, rather than listening

- Discuss your lists with a partner.
- Do you both agree with the way you have assessed your own strengths and weaknesses?

CHECK YOUR LEARNING – STRENGTHS AND WEAKNESSES

1. Explain in your own words what each of the following terms means. Give examples.

   - Self-confidence
   - Self-esteem
   - Self-worth

2. Outline a situation which could lead to a young person feeling a lack of self-confidence. What advice could you give to this person to try to help them feel positive about themselves?

3. What difficulties might be experienced in relationships with others? How might these difficulties affect a person's self-worth?

4. Explain how parents can help their teenage children to have higher self-esteem.

SETTING TARGETS AND WORKING TOWARDS GOALS

WHAT DO WE MEAN BY TARGETS AND GOALS?

In sports, most people understand exactly what we mean by targets and goals. A goal is a hoop, area or cage and the objective of many team games is to get the ball into it or through it, to score as highly as possible and be the winner. A target, used in shooting or archery, is something to aim at.

These terms are also used to refer to our ambitions and hopes for the future.

Whatever stage of life someone is at, whether a student at school, an employee, or a retired person, it is important to have something to aim for or focus on, in order to have a sense of achievement. This could be doing well in exams, getting an important promotion, or perhaps taking up a new hobby or interest. Setting targets and working towards goals is an important part of life. They can help to give meaning and purpose – and when achieved, can be a big boost to a person's self-confidence and self-esteem.

WHAT IS THE DIFFERENCE BETWEEN A TARGET AND A GOAL?

In life terms, a goal is the final aim, the end result that a person wants to achieve. To reach this goal, it is necessary to plan to make it happen. You cannot achieve a goal immediately and it does not just happen by itself. Instead, you must usually take several steps towards achieving your goal. These stages towards the goal are the targets.

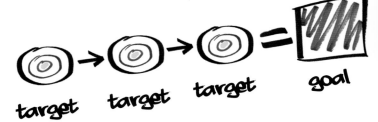

A goal will tend to be long term, while the targets to reach it will be medium or short term. By carefully planning these targets, the goal can be achieved.

Many people have goals, dreams, ideas, visions and plans for the future, but they never happen. Why?

Often it is because they are not planned through a series of appropriate targets.

CASE STUDY – KATIE

Katie is studying for her GCSEs. She hopes to do well so she can return to school for Sixth Form. She would like to do a BSc in Nursing at University.

Katie's goal: To get good grades in her GCSEs.
Katie's targets:
- Sort out all her notes.
- Complete outstanding coursework.
- Keep up to date with all homework.
- Ask teachers about anything she does not understand.
- Make a revision plan – and start immediately.

CASE STUDY – ASH

Ash loves cars and wants to learn to drive as soon as possible. He is still at school, studying for AS Levels, but will be seventeen in a couple of month's time.

Ash's goal: To start driving lessons as soon as he is old enough.

Ash's targets:

- Talk to his dad about whether he can go on the insurance for the family car.
- Talk to his mum about helping out around the house for extra money.
- Try to get a part time job.
- Drop hints that he would like driving lessons as a birthday present.
- Phone local driving schools to find out the best prices.
- Apply for his provisional license.

CASE STUDY – CLASS 12G

The Year 12s have been learning about Fair Trade. Class 12G have decided that it is important to raise awareness about some of the issues involved.

12G's goal: To organise a Fair Trade Week in school.

12G's targets:

- Get permission from the Principal (the class teacher can do this).
- Speak in assembly to other year groups (Julie and Sam are good at speaking in public).
- Produce posters for school notice boards (Rory and Claire do GCSE Art; they can get to work on the posters).
- Arrange for speakers to come into school. (Anne, Kieran and Joel can do this; they are good at organising things).

Setting targets and working towards goals is not just an individual process. A group of people might decide on a goal that they all want to work towards. Together they will decide the targets which will lead them to achieve this. Not everyone in the group may have the same targets; these may differ according to individual strengths and weaknesses. However, all people in the group will be working towards a common goal. Self-confidence can be improved as people work together, each making their own valuable contribution to the project.

ACTIVITY

John loves online gaming and spends most of his free time on the computer. He knows he is really unfit, but three of his friends have persuaded him to enter the Belfast Marathon with them as a relay team. The marathon is six months away.

Work out John's goal and set targets to help him achieve this.

BEING SUCCESSFUL AND ACHIEVING GOALS

Some goals cannot be achieved as they are unrealistic. Not everybody can be a professional footballer, pop star or astronaut, no matter how carefully chosen and planned the targets are! While it is important to aim high to give yourself a challenge, it can also be very demoralising if goals are never reached. There needs to be a chance of achieving them. Also, goals which are too broad and lack focus often end up unachieved.

The letters of the word **SMART** are sometimes used to describe successful goals.

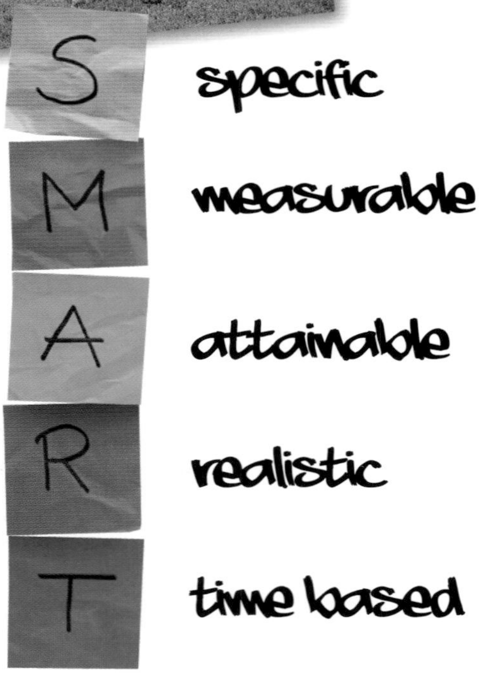

S specific

M measurable

A attainable

R realistic

T time based

WHAT IS A SMART GOAL?

Specific: Goals should be straightforward and show clearly what you want to happen. They should also be something important to you or you will lack the motivation to achieve it.

Measurable: A successful goal is one that is measurable. This means that you know how far away your goal is and when it has been reached.

Attainable: When you identify the goals that you want to achieve, then you begin to figure out ways to make them come true. You will probably give up on a goal that is too far out of reach. A goal needs to be a challenge, but not impossible.

Realistic: A goal that is realistic is not too difficult (which could result in failure) or too easy (as this does not give a sense of achievement).

Time based: There needs to be a realistic timeframe for the goal, so you know exactly what you are committing to. A time limit can give a sense of urgency – you need to start working towards your goal now!

DISCUSSION

Discuss in pairs or threes. What are some long-term and short-term goals in your life? What targets do you have for getting there?

ACTIVITY

- Decide on a personal goal.
- Write a series of targets that will help you achieve this goal.

PRESSURES ON YOUNG PEOPLE

WHAT PRESSURES ARE THERE?

Some people believe that young people are under much more pressure today than in the past, for example, when their parents were teenagers. Statistics show that over the last thirty years there has been an increase in the number of suicides and incidences of self-harm among teenagers. Modern life puts many pressures on young people – to do well in education and work; to look good and have the right things; to cope with problems in family life and to try and achieve their goals for the future. Sometimes these pressures of life can seem like too much to cope with and lead to feelings of despair and hopelessness.

There are both external and internal pressures in a person's life:

External pressure comes from influences outside us, such as friends, family, school, the media and peer group.

Internal pressure comes from within and is what motivates us to achieve our goals and ambitions, dreams and plans for the future.

Pressures can be both positive and negative. A good friend may encourage you to do well in your exams or to take up a particular hobby or sport. Sometimes friends can have a bad effect, encouraging you to take part in activities you would not do otherwise, such as shop-lifting or substance abuse. Most parents want what is best for their child and will offer positive encouragement. However, family problems such as divorce or illness can lead to negative pressure on a young person.

Taking part in a sport or being a member of a club can have a positive effect, as it may encourage commitment and give a sense of achievement.

A church or religion may also put positive pressure on a young person, by encouraging a different set of standards and values to those often put across by the media or peer group. A person with a strong religious faith may have a high sense of their own self-worth.

THE EFFECTS OF PRESSURE

Pressure can be positive, in that it can motivate and inspire and help to achieve goals. A person's ability to cope with pressure can be affected by the number of problems or issues they are trying to cope with at the time, and the support systems they have in place. However, too much pressure, particularly if it is negative, can jeopardise your health and well-being and relationships with family and friends, compromise your morals, and distract you from everything you'd planned to do in the future.

Sometimes too much negative pressure can lead to depression, which can make someone feel worried and bad-tempered, or give symptoms such as stomach pains or headaches. Some people experience sleep difficulties as a sign of depression or perhaps turn to drug or alcohol abuse. Others may lose all interest in hobbies or school work.

Negative pressure can become so overwhelming for some young people that they see suicide as the only answer to their problems. It may seem that life is not worth living, or that this is the only way to draw attention to how unhappy they are.

Self-harm is where a person may deliberately hurt themselves, for example, by cutting their skin. This is also associated with depression and feelings of despair. Depression needs to be taken seriously and sufferers need expert help and counselling.

It is important to talk to someone if you have ever self-harmed, or considered it, or ever thought about suicide. You could speak to someone you know and trust, or to an anonymous voice on the phone, but it is essential to get help. Here are some suggestions:

Talk to a parent, relative, teacher or school counsellor. It is good to talk to someone you know and trust, and they can help you get the help you need.

Alternatively, you can talk to someone anonymously at one of these organisations:

CONTACT YOUTH is a counselling service for young people in Northern Ireland.

02890 744499 for the Head Office in Belfast

0808 808 8000 for LIFELINE 24/7 suicide prevention

www.contactyouth.org

CHILDLINE is a free and confidential helpline for children and young adults. You can get help and advice from a counsellor over the telephone or online.

0800 11 11   www.childline.org

SAMARITANS offers confidential emotional support on any subject for people of any age.

08457 90 90 90   www.samaritans.org
                        jo@samaritans.org

There is more information on self-harm and suicide on page 62.

PEER PRESSURE

Peers are people of your own age. Everyone is part of a peer group, no matter how old they are. Adults are part of a peer group, and may feel the effects of peer pressure. Adults may feel under pressure in their job to work extra hours or meet certain standards. At home, they may face pressure from neighbours to keep the garden neat and tidy. However, the term 'peer pressure' is usually used to refer to young people, particularly those of secondary school age. Peer pressure is when a friend, or group of friends, tries to persuade you to do something you are uncomfortable with. While peer pressure can sometimes be positive, all too often it is negative and a young person may feel pressured into:

- Smoking, drinking or taking drugs;
- Stealing or shoplifting;
- Fighting or vandalism;
- Truancy or ignoring schoolwork;
- Joining in with bullying others;
- Having a sexual relationship when they don't want to.

Anyone who refuses to join in may end up being bullied themselves or excluded from the group. It is important to choose friends carefully as a true friend will not usually put their friends under this kind of pressure. It is also important to know your own mind, be prepared to stand up to people and do what you think is right. There are certain situations a young person may find themselves in, which make it more likely that they will give in to negative peer pressure. These may include having little or no self-confidence, low self-esteem, often feeling lonely and isolated and having few close friendships.

FAMILY PRESSURE

Family life is never perfect, and the family that never has any arguments, tensions or problems does not exist. You may feel under pressure because your parents' or carers' idea of what is best for you is different to your own or because a younger brother or sister is really annoying. However, many of the pressures of family life can be an important part of learning to live with other people and being tolerant to the needs of others.

Sometimes family life may be affected by a particular crisis, which can lead to negative pressure on a young person. Here are some examples:

Family break up: When a relationship ends in separation or divorce this can be very stressful for everyone in the family, particularly the children. Following a family break up, children may have to get used to seeing much less of one parent, perhaps just visiting at the weekends. There may be less money to spend as the single parent tries to manage the household budget on one wage. A young person might feel guilty, believing that they are partly responsible for their parents' divorce. It may be necessary for the family to move house, and for the children to move to a new school, bringing more change and stress.

Re-marriage: A young person may also feel negative pressure if a parent finds a new partner and re-marries. Having to adjust to a blended family, with a step-parent and possibly step-siblings, could be very stressful.

Bereavement: The death of a close family member is one of the most difficult situations that anyone can face. If the death was sudden, there may be feelings of shock and disbelief. In the case of a terminal illness, there may have been a long period of anxiety leading up to the death. There may be feelings of guilt if a member of the family has died by suicide. Children who are coping with bereavement in the family can experience feelings of isolation, shock and distress. Teenagers may become withdrawn, or perhaps take risks with drugs and alcohol, as a reaction to what has happened.

Young carers: It is good for children in a family to take on responsibility, even when they are young. However, some children are under huge pressure as they have to care for a parent, perhaps because of disability, illness or an addiction problem. Most young carers are between eight and fifteen years old, although some are as young as five. Sometimes a young carer will have to look after a younger brother or sister, or perhaps a grandparent, who is suffering illness or disability. Young carers may have to take on many of the household jobs, and might be responsible for the shopping, cleaning and cooking. They may also have to give physical care, such as bathing and feeding the person who is ill. A young carer may have to deal with difficult and stressful situations at home; for example, a parent who has been drinking heavily, or a brother or sister who is experiencing severe pain.

Abuse: Abuse is when a person suffers cruel or hurtful treatment from another person. Abuse can happen anywhere, but it can be particularly traumatic if it is experienced at home or inflicted by a member of the family.

Physical abuse involves hitting, punching, kicking or hurting someone else. **Sexual abuse** is when sexual contact is forced on someone. This type of abuse is particularly serious if the abuser is in a position of trust and should be caring for the person they are hurting. **Emotional abuse** is when a person deliberately tries to make someone else feel inadequate and worthless. For example, a child may be shouted at and bullied so that he or she feels intimidated, ashamed or unfairly criticised. A child who is emotionally abused receives no positive emotional support from parents or carers. **Neglect**, where parents or carers deliberately ignore their child's physical needs, is also a type of abuse. No one should feel so pressured by their family that they feel in danger either physically or mentally.

evaluation

Evaluate how family relationships can have an effect on a young person's self-confidence and self-esteem.

PRESSURE FROM THE MEDIA

The term 'media' refers to the following:

- Newspapers, magazines and books;
- Television, films and the radio;
- Video games;
- Billboards and posters.

The media can have a huge impact on our moral standards, what we buy and how we see ourselves. Many people's ideas about the world are based on what they read, see or hear in the media. Media pressure can be very subtle, as people can be influenced without even realising it. The media can sometimes have a very positive influence; for example, through television programmes, books and articles that are educational and thought-provoking. However, it is important to be selective, as many of the messages put across by the media can have a negative effect.

Television: TV programmes often portray images that are stereotypes; for example, an 'ideal' family might be portrayed and people might be pressured to be like the family in the television series. Soap operas often have affairs, scandals and broken relationships as a storyline and this can give the impression that these activities are normal behaviour for everyone.

Magazines: Glamour magazines are popular as they contain glossy pictures of attractive and famous celebrities. They often give an unrealistic impression of how people should look, especially when it comes to body shape. Many people feel that fashion pages which only show very thin models could be a reason why some young people suffer from eating disorders.

Magazines aimed at teenagers often contain articles about sex and relationships, which can be very misleading as they often imply that almost all teenagers are sexually active. Again, this can put negative pressure on young people to have a relationship for which they are not ready.

DISCUSSION

- How have you been influenced by TV and magazines? Perhaps you might have bought a product that you have seen advertised.
- Can you think of any other examples?
- How do you think television programmes have shaped your attitudes and opinions?

THE INTERNET

Using the Internet can be educational, fun, a great way to stay in touch with friends, and can give access to games, films and music. However, it is sensible to be aware of the potential dangers and negative influences, as well as the many benefits of going online. Not all sites contain factual or reliable information and there is the risk of accessing sites with offensive material.

Chat rooms can be entertaining and seem harmless, but talking to people you cannot see could be risky as people can tell lies. In a chat room, it is sensible to keep messages public unless you know the person in real life; do not join a private chat room with a stranger as it is easier for them to annoy or upset you.

Never give out photos or personal information to a stranger online – and never arrange to meet anyone you chat to online.

Social networking is becoming very popular, but think carefully about what personal information you are making available for everyone to read.

NEWS ITEM

A man is being questioned after the body of a teenager he is believed to have met on the Internet was discovered in a field in County Durham.

The body of Ashleigh Hall, 17, was found after the arrest of a 32-year-old man for traffic offences on the A177 near Sedgefield on Monday night. Durham Police said the Darlington girl told family she was staying with a friend on Sunday night.

The arrested man is being questioned on suspicion of murder. Police said he had given them several different names and had yet to be identified.

The teenager had told her family she would be home by lunchtime on Monday. When she failed to return, her mother repeatedly rang her mobile phone, but could not get a reply.

Ashleigh's body was found fully clothed near the Little Chef roundabout off the A689 and A177 and it is believed it could have been there for up to 24 hours. It was removed from the field by officers on Tuesday afternoon and taken to Darlington Memorial Hospital. A post-mortem examination is due to be carried

out, but currently there is no indication that she was sexually assaulted, said police.

Detective Chief Inspector Paul Harker urged parents to monitor their children's online habits. He said: "This is a very, very unusual event. My message in terms of meeting people from the Internet is 'please do not do it unless you are absolutely certain it is safe'". He added: "Speak to them about it, speak to their friends, let them know the dangers of the Internet."

Source: http://news.bbc.co.uk/1/hi/england/wear/8327310.stm

....

ACTIVITIES

1) *Work in pairs*
Role play a conversation between two friends. One has told the other – in strict confidence – that they are going to meet someone they have been chatting to online. In your role play, try to present some convincing arguments why this is not a good idea.

2) Design a poster, suitable for display in a Primary school classroom, warning children of the dangers that can be associated with the Internet.

....

Cyberbullying is the use of electronic communication, such as email, text messages, mobile phones, chat rooms or blogs to bully, insult or threaten another person. Some people may mistakenly think that this kind of behaviour is just a 'joke' but it is illegal and very distressing for the victim.

Online gambling is becoming increasingly popular. The games can be good fun and young people can only legally play for free. However, there are risks attached as these free sites could encourage addiction. A possible consequence of this could be serious debt and a gambling problem in later life.

SCHOOL PRESSURE

Pressure to do well: It is to be expected that a good school will want to help each pupil reach the highest standard they are capable of . This may include academic success and the opportunity to achieve in sport, music, drama and many other activities.

However, some pupils feel under tremendous pressure to perform well at school, which can lead to anxiety and tension. Perhaps a young person finds some subjects difficult and struggles to keep up. The situation can be made worse if the teacher sees these difficulties as a lack of effort. Even very able students can feel under pressure to keep up the high standard expected of them.

Exams: This can be a very stressful time for students of all abilities. It can be a positive experience to feel some tension and anxiety, as the person who is too laid back is not motivated to do anything! However, there needs to be a sensible balance. During exam time, revision needs to be carefully planned to avoid last-minute panics and late-night cramming sessions.

It is important to remember a healthy diet, exercise and sufficient sleep as ways of helping yourself to do your best.

Bullying: Sadly, bullying is a fact of life for many school pupils. In 1999, all schools in the UK had to introduce an anti-bullying policy, but research has shown that levels of bullying have either stayed the same or become worse. Surveys on bullying indicate that 1 in 5 teenagers has been bullied, while 1 in 10 admits to bullying others. Bullying includes inflicting physical pain, such as hitting, kicking or punching

and making verbal assaults such as name-calling, telling lies about someone or making remarks about appearance or ethnic origin. A subtle, but particularly painful, type of bullying is being ignored

or excluded from group activities. Being bullied can make a pupil feel frightened, powerless and unwilling to come to school. This negative pressure can lead to a fall in the standard of a young person's schoolwork and a loss of confidence in their own abilities. It is important for a pupil who is being bullied at school to tell someone they trust so something can be done about it.

For some pupils, school becomes such a stressful experience that they may refuse to attend. This may be because of bullying, inability to cope with work, or because other emotional worries make school seem unimportant. Many schools nowadays recognise the pressures faced by their pupils and offer a counselling service.

STRATEGIES TO HELP COPE WITH PRESSURE

When pressure feels like it is becoming too much to handle, it is important to find a way to cope with the stress and tension. Some people turn to destructive activities to try and cope with stress, such as substance abuse or self-harm, but these only make matters worse. There are many positive ways to deal with pressure:

Playing sport: Physical exercise can help to relieve tension and is a way to forget about emotional issues, even if it is only temporary. If academic studies are not going well

at school, it can raise self-esteem to be successful at something else.

Talk to a friend: It is important to feel that you are not alone, that there is someone who is on your side. Parents and friends may have some useful advice.

Set achievable targets: This may be an effective strategy to try and sort out problems with school work and pressure at school (read about setting goals and targets on pages 30 – 32).

Be assertive: This does not mean pushing other people around, but sometimes it is important to stand up for yourself, for example, if you are being bullied. Let people see that you are not going to accept unkind or unfair treatment.

Try to compromise: Sometimes the best policy is to try and reach an agreement, especially if your idea about what is best for you is different to that of a parent or teacher.

Find some personal space: Finding time for yourself can be an effective way of coping with pressure. If problems at home are making life difficult, then getting out of the house for a while, perhaps to go for a walk, can help relieve stress.

DISCUSSION
What do you do to cope with pressure?

CHECK YOUR LEARNING – PRESSURE

- Choose two examples of positive pressure and explain how they can be of benefit to a person.
- Choose two examples of negative pressure and explain how they can be damaging to a person.
- Explain what is meant by each of the following: *Peer pressure; cyberbullying; media pressure.*
- Explain some of the ways the media can put pressure on a young person.
- Suggest ways in which schools can help their pupils cope with negative pressure.

EXTENSION TASK
Read the following news report.
Select some of the facts given in this report to write your own article for a school magazine. You may wish to balance your article by including alternative viewpoints, such as positive pressures on young people and help and support available.

NEWS ITEM

PUPILS 'UNDER GREATER PRESSURE'
More than 70% of teachers think pupils are under more pressure now than they were 10 years ago, a survey suggests.

Exam pressures and family break-up were thought to be the main stress points, the questionnaire by the Association of Teachers and Lecturers found. Of the 700 teachers who completed the ATL questionnaire, 52% thought pressure to be popular on social networking sites was also a source of strain. Cyberbullying, such as abusive texts and e-mails, was also deemed a stress. More than half of those surveyed felt pupils were under more pressure now than two years ago and over 70% felt pupils currently faced more pressure than 10 years ago.

Family break-up (mentioned by 76%), teacher and school pressure to do well (mentioned by 55%), body image and pressure to look good (mentioned by 55%) and lack of parental support (mentioned by 54%) were cited as the major factors contributing to pupil stress.

The majority of respondents (81%) noted that stressed pupils experienced low self-esteem, 78% said these pupils lacked motivation and 74% said they had witnessed pupils crying due to the pressures they faced. Many teachers said they had witnessed physical effects of pressure on pupils. 43% said pupils in their school had self-harmed due to the pressures they faced, 37% said students suffered from eating disorders and 13% knew of a pupil who had attempted suicide. Of those questioned, 73% said their school offered pupils access to a counsellor.

Story from BBC NEWS 2009/04/08
Source: http://news.bbc.co.uk/1/hi/education/7987633.stm

EXAM FOCUS

In chapter one, we looked at the skill of clearly demonstrating your knowledge and understanding.

The following question will give you further practice at this:

(a) Name two examples of a personal goal.

[2 marks]

(b) Identify and explain two factors which can have an influence on a person's self-esteem.

[4 marks]

(c) Identify and explain two ways in which a young person may experience negative pressure.

[4 marks]

Remember to start (b) and (c) by stating clearly what you have chosen to write about, and then develop your explanation.

You could begin part (c) in the following way:

'Family pressure – There could be a lot of arguments at home due to a marriage break up, with the children being unhappy and unsettled. If a parent re-marries this can also put negative pressure on a young person, especially if there are step brothers and sisters to get used to.'

Continue this answer adding an example of your own.

TIME

1 hour 30

INSTRUC

Write you
Answer **a**

INFORMA

The total m
Quality of
Figures in b
question or

ADVICE TO

You are advi
examination

d to each

lable

Chapter three

BUILDING AND MAINTAINING HEALTHY RELATIONSHIPS

CHAPTER SUMMARY

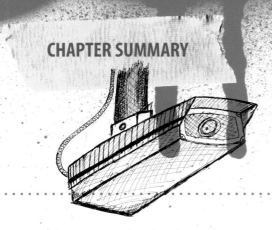

In this chapter you will be studying:
- **The characteristics of a healthy relationship.**
- **Family relationships.**
- **Relationships with friends and peer group.**
- **Sexual relationships.**

HEALTHY RELATIONSHIPS

WHAT IS A HEALTHY RELATIONSHIP?

A healthy relationship is one that will make you feel good about yourself. You should feel safe being in the company of the other person, knowing that you can trust them and that they want what is best for you. In a healthy relationship, you know that you are valued. An unhealthy relationship is one which makes a person feel scared, anxious or angry.

A healthy peer relationship will involve an equal balance of power, where one person is not dominated by the other. There should be an equal amount of give and take; one person should not feel that they are the one making all the effort in the relationship.

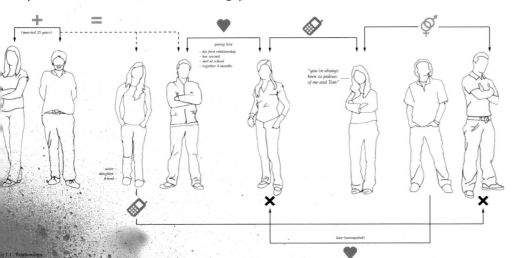

Finally, a healthy relationship is one that is enjoyable; it is fun being in a particular person's company and you do it through choice, not because you have to. You do activities together that you both enjoy.

As a teenager, you will have different relationships with lots of different people – members of your family, friendships with other young people both inside and outside of school, and dating relationships with a girlfriend or boyfriend. Relationships made during teenage years are often an important part of maturing and learning about the kind of person you are. Learning to build healthy relationships as a young person can help you to develop and maintain healthy relationships with the people you will meet throughout life.

"if you have to keep a **relationship** secret, you shouldn't be in it"

A person has the power to create healthy relationships around them – they do not just happen by accident. Relationships with others can be the best part of people's lives, but they can also be the most challenging. Building healthy relationships is a process that never ends.

POSITIVE FACTORS IN A HEALTHY RELATIONSHIP

Building and maintaining healthy relationships takes time, energy and effort. No two relationships will be the same, but a healthy relationship is likely to include some or all of the following qualities:

Mutual respect: An important quality of a healthy relationship is that the people involved respect each other for who they are. There will be a strong sense of each other's value as a person.

Communication: In a relationship, people should be able to talk and listen to each other. Sharing thoughts and feelings with another person is a way of showing how important they are in your life.

Honesty: While it is necessary to respect other people's feelings in a relationship, honesty is also important. This means not telling lies. However, some situations require tact and sensitivity.

Tolerance: This means respecting the fact that everyone is different; a healthy relationship is one which can cope with other people's weaknesses and annoying habits.

Trust: In healthy relationships, people trust each other; they know they can rely on the other person for support and that secrets will not be gossiped about.

Commitment: Building healthy relationships takes time and effort. The people involved need to be determined to make the relationship work and to try and overcome any difficulties that may arise.

Sharing: The degree of sharing depends on the relationship. This can mean sharing your thoughts and feelings with another person, sharing a few hours of your time as you take part in an activity together, or sharing your life with someone.

A degree of independence: An important part of all good relationships is being able to depend on one another. However, it is also important to have a degree of independence. In a healthy friendship one person will not try to dominate the other. In family relationships, Parents need to let their children have freedom to make some decisions for themselves as they mature.

Compromise: Arguments and disagreements are to be expected from time to time in any relationship. One of the signs of a healthy relationship is that the people involved can talk things over and reach a decision that suits both of them. Working through a disagreement and reaching a compromise can help to make a relationship stronger.

Forgiveness: No-one is perfect; people upset and disappoint each other often without meaning to. This is why forgiveness is important in a healthy relationship.

Accepting responsibility for your actions: If a relationship is in difficulty, it is usually not the fault of one person. Both people involved need to accept responsibility for making it work. On the other hand, if you know you have behaved badly towards another person, it is important to make amends.

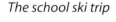

ACTIVITY

Work in pairs for this activity
Look the following situations. Discuss which factor from the list above is missing from each relationship.

The school ski trip

"It's really unfair! I'm not allowed to go on the ski trip. Mum says we can't afford it and she has the rest of the family to think about. She's being really mean!"

A worried parent

"Dad can't seem to realise that I'm nearly seventeen! He says he is 'worried about me' going to Mark's party. There's no point talking to him, he never listens. I don't care, I'm going anyway. I'll tell him I'm babysitting."

The party

"I'm asking Cathy to go with me to the party... okay, I'm still dating Beth, but she's away for the weekend. It's all right, she won't find out."

A friend's secret

"You'll never guess what's happened to Sophie! Of course, I was told in confidence as I'm her best friend, but just wait till you hear this..."

Gran's operation

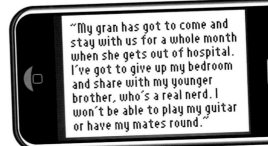

"My gran has got to come and stay with us for a whole month when she gets out of hospital. I've got to give up my bedroom and share with my younger brother, who's a real nerd. I won't be able to play my guitar or have my mates round."

43

FAMILY RELATIONSHIPS

Healthy family relationships can help to create strong, healthy individuals. The family home is where most people learn how to relate with other people and cope with life in the outside world. We can choose our friends but we cannot choose our family, so sometimes more effort is needed to build good relationships.

FAMILIES : SOME DEFINITIONS

Single parent family – A parent is raising children on their own, perhaps due to divorce, bereavement or never having been married.

Extended family – Parents and children, plus other relatives, such as grandparents, living in the family home.

Foster family – Family care for a child whose own parents are facing a crisis; a foster family will provide temporary care.

Adoptive family – Permanent care for a child where this cannot be provided by the birth parents; adoptive parents have full legal responsibility for the child.

Step-family – If a parent remarries, a child will have a step-parent and possibly step-brothers and sisters in their new family.

Blended family – This term is sometimes used to describe a family that includes children from previous marriages and younger siblings from a new marriage.

HEALTHY FAMILY RELATIONSHIPS

Good communication is very important in a family relationship. Taking the time to talk – and listen – to others in the family can help to ensure that family relationships stay strong and happy. Research has shown that good communication between parents and children can lead to fewer behaviour problems when young people reach their teens.

It is also important to learn how to handle conflict, by trying to avoid fighting and arguments and aiming for a compromise instead. Reaching a compromise is all about negotiation. This means calmly explaining your point of view and listening to what the other person has to say; the next stage is to work out a way forward that is acceptable to everyone involved.

Some conflicts in families are about small things; it might be best to let these things go and concentrate on the bigger issues. It is not unhealthy to have conflict in families, but it is important to handle it well. Everyone involved should feel happy with the outcome with no-one feeling hurt through another person's anger. Handling conflict well can lead to healthier and stronger relationships.

When children are very young they rely on their parents and carers to do everything for them and this includes making decisions on their behalf. As children grow older, they need greater independence. This means being willing to help out with the day-to-day responsibilities to be done in the home, but also having a role to play in decision making.

Having greater independence is particularly important for teenagers, to help them grow into responsible adults who can make sensible choices for themselves. However, this has to be balanced against concerns for the young person's safety, especially with night-time activities. Negotiation and compromise can be important here. Parents may need to consider new rules, but young people must be able to convince parents that they are ready for greater responsibility.

Johnny is 16 years old and he really wants a part time job and his own transport. He has been given the offer of work at a local takeaway food shop, and this will involve working on Thursday, Friday and Saturday evenings. He will have to work very late on Friday – until 2am – but this means he will be able save up for a motor scooter. Johnny's parents have the following concerns:

- *His school work will suffer;*
- *He will be out later than he is normally allowed to be on a Friday;*
- *They are worried about his safety on a scooter.*

In groups of about 3, script or role play a situation where Johnny tries to convince his parents that he will be responsible if given greater freedom.

Healthy family relationships involve people caring for each other. They try to be positive even if someone has made a mistake. In a healthy family relationship, family members offer encouragement to each other and try to promote one another's self-esteem.

Forgiveness is also very important in family life. No-one is perfect and from time to time everyone says or does things that cause hurt and upset. This is why forgiveness is a vital part of healthy family relationships. If someone in the family will not forgive, this can create an unequal relationship. The person who has made the mistake can be made to feel that they owe something to the person who has been wronged.

BROTHERS AND SISTERS

Some young people are very different to their brothers and sisters, even though they are growing up in the same family. There can be feelings of jealousy and insecurity if someone thinks their brother or sister is more intelligent or more popular than they are. Sibling rivalry is where the children in a family compare themselves to each other and compete for their parents' attention. This can lead to fights, arguing and name-calling.

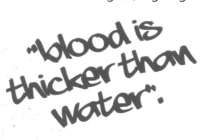

"blood is thicker than water".

It can take a special effort to build healthy relationships with brothers and sisters – especially if they are very annoying! A younger brother might keep going into your room and taking your things, while an older sister may boss you around and tell you what to do. Trying to avoid fighting and trying to reach a compromise could be especially valuable in situations such as these. Sometimes sharing an activity together that you both enjoy could lead to a more positive relationship. Brothers and sisters can often grow up to be the best of friends and have a special bond which can last for life.

Family relationships can be really good because…

- You live closely with members of your family and do lots of things together.
- You can relax and be yourself when you are with close family.
- Members of the same family often share the same characteristics, likes and dislikes.
- They put up with you, even if you are in a bad mood.
- You know your family will always support you whatever happens.

…on the other hand, they can also be difficult

- Family members can often be very blunt and outspoken when pointing out one another's faults.
- Family arguments can sometimes be the worst.
- If you are having problems with a family member, you cannot just walk away as you have to live with that person.
- Families know each other really well, but this means they also know how to tease, upset and annoy each other.
- Sometimes members of your family can embarrass you in front of your friends.
- Sadly, sometimes families do not care for each other. When family relations completely break down this is called a 'dysfunctional family'.

FRIENDSHIPS

Outside of our families, some of the closest and most long-lasting relationships of our lives will be with friends. Sometimes we choose to be friends with a person because we like or admire them. Other friendships just happen, perhaps because we spend a lot of time together in class, or have a shared interest.

Friendships play a very important part in life, particularly for teenagers. You may feel that your family does not understand your problems, but a close friend your own age can relate to what you are going through. Friendships also encourage independence from your family and open up opportunities, such as trying a new activity or joining a club. Most people enjoy the company of others; building good relationships with other people can have a positive effect on a person's self-esteem and sense of self-worth. Friends are really important, no matter how long a friendship lasts.

ACTIVITY

Discuss the following questions in small groups:

- Which do you think is best – a small circle of close friends or a large group of casual acquaintances?
- Consider the friendships you have now. For how long have these friendships lasted? Does anyone have a friendship going back to P1 (or earlier)?
- Are your friends mostly around your own age and from a similar background, or are these factors unimportant?
- What do you consider to be the ingredients of a successful friendship?
- What personal qualities do you consider important in a friend?
- Do your friends see these qualities in you?

HEALTHY RELATIONSHIPS WITH FRIENDS

Many people would agree that mutual respect is a necessary ingredient in a friendship. It is important to feel accepted for who we are and to accept others. With close friends it is good to be able to relax and be ourselves. True friends do not put pressure on you to take part in activities you are not comfortable with. As with any healthy relationship, communication is necessary so that a friendship can develop and become strong. This will lead to a good understanding between friends.

If there is an argument or disagreement this does not necessarily mean that the relationship is unhealthy. As long as friends can talk to one another and are prepared to listen to each other, they should be able to resolve a conflict. Healthy friendships involve respecting each other's differences.

There is a sense of sharing in a healthy friendship, with close friends spending time in each other's company, perhaps taking part in the same activities. Friends often share likes and dislikes, hobbies and interests.

Trust is essential in building a strong friendship. It is important to be able to share secrets with a friend without worrying that they will be passed on to others. Closely associated with trust is loyalty. True friends are the ones you know will always stand by you, no matter what happens. In a healthy relationship, friends do their best to keep their promises and do not usually let each other down. Where there is trust, there is probably honesty as well. You can rely on your friend to tell you if your new outfit or hairstyle really is dreadful; however, you also know your

friend will be tactful and show consideration for your feelings. Good friends care; they show kindness and support each other through difficulties.

No relationship is perfect and friends will let each other down and hurt each other's feelings, often without meaning to. This is why forgiveness is an important quality in a healthy friendship. The strongest bonds are usually those where friends show the most forgiveness towards each other.

Healthy friendships are those where there is equality in the relationship; one person will not attempt to dominate the other by making all the decisions, or telling their friend what to wear and who to talk to. Friends also need to accept responsibility for the relationship, by both putting in an effort to make it strong. It is important never to take our friends for granted. Through friendships we can learn about the qualities we would expect to see in others and how we can show these qualities ourselves.

ACTIVITY

Choose five of the factors listed on pages 42 – 43.

- Score each of them out of 10 according to how important you think they are in a healthy friendship.
- Explain your choices in a short paragraph.

WHEN A FRIEND NEEDS SUPPORT...

A sign of a strong, healthy friendship is that a friend will turn to you for support when they are faced with a difficult situation. For example, this could be because your friend:

- *is unhappy at home, perhaps as a result of parents fighting;*
- *has just ended a relationship with a girlfriend or boyfriend;*
- *is in trouble at school;*
- *has to cope with a health problem, concerning themselves or a family member;*

- has not been accepted for a school team or drama production;
- is disappointed with exam results.

DISCUSSION
What would you do to help a friend in these situations?

YOU COULD HELP IN THE FOLLOWING WAYS...

One of the most important ways in which you could support your friend is simply to be there and offer a sympathetic ear. This could involve:

- setting aside time to talk to your friend;
- being sympathetic and letting your friend know that you are concerned;
- carefully asking questions and finding out what you can do about the situation;
- listening without passing judgement or making criticisms;
- planning an activity to help your friend forget about their worries for a while;
- encouraging your friend to get help from a sympathetic adult if the problem is serious.

SEXUAL RELATIONSHIPS

There is no correct age to begin dating; everybody is different and individual families will have their own rules. When you decide to start a relationship, it should be because you genuinely care about that person, not just because you want a boyfriend or girlfriend – or because your friends think you should be dating. It is better not to rush into anything too quickly.

It is also important to remember that a relationship which involves sexual feelings does not have to mean actually having sex. A person may not feel that this level of intimacy and commitment is right with everyone they go out with. In fact, they may feel that it is not appropriate at all until they are married or in a committed relationship.

Celibacy means choosing not to have a sexual relationship. This may be a decision for life, perhaps because of a religious commitment. Some people may decide to remain celibate until they are married, or at least in a serious and loving relationship. It is perfectly okay to choose not to have sex in a relationship and it is important that both people respect each others limits. Virginity should not be seen as a burden or embarrassment – and remember that many young people who boast about their sexual activities probably have a very active imagination!

Sometimes dating relationships are better in a group, where two or three couples might take part in an activity, such as going to the cinema or ten-pin bowling. This way there could be less unwelcome pressure to be too intimate early on in a relationship.

HEALTHY DATING RELATIONSHIPS

The ingredients of a healthy friendship – such as **trust, honesty, consideration, loyalty, forgiveness** and **sharing** – will also be present in a healthy dating relationship, too.

However, dating relationships are different as they also include physical affection, such as holding hands, hugging and kissing. Therefore respect is especially important, as no-one should feel pressured into intimacy they do not want or are not ready for. Some young people end up having sex in a relationship, not because they want to, but because they feel under pressure from their partner. In a healthy sexual relationship a person should not be afraid to say no; there is no obligation to agree to everything your partner asks. Standing up for yourself can improve trust in a relationship as your boyfriend or girlfriend will know what your personal standards and values are. It is also important to be consistent, so that words and body language convey the same message. Try not to give the wrong impression!

It probably does not matter to you what your friends look like, but as a dating relationship will involve some degree of physical attraction, a dating partner's looks may well be important. In fact, physical appearance is often what leads two people to be attracted to each other in the first place. However, a relationship which is just based on physical attraction alone will not last for very long. A strong, healthy relationship will be based on someone's character – that you like them as a person, find them fun to be with and enjoy their company.

Independence is another quality that should be present in a healthy dating relationship. While the couple who are dating will want to spend time in each other's company, it is also healthy to spend some time apart and maintain existing friendships. A dating partner should not be jealous or possessive, getting angry if you talk to friends of the opposite sex. This is a sign of an unhealthy relationship.

WHEN A RELATIONSHIP NEEDS TO END. . .

Unlike some other relationships we make, sometimes dating relationships don't last very long. This is particularly true during teenage years – you may be madly in love with someone one week and completely turned off them the next!

All relationships go through difficult times and if it was a strong one to begin with, then it is more likely to survive. However, if you are no longer finding a relationship satisfying and enjoyable, especially a dating relationship, then it might be time for it to end. If you have begun to feel anxious about a relationship you are in, or you feel threatened in any way, then you should end it immediately. For example:

• If the person you are dating abuses alcohol or drugs and wants you to do the same;

• If your partner puts pressure on you to take part in sexual activities you do not feel comfortable with, perhaps applying emotional pressure such as "If you loved me, you would do it…"

- Your girlfriend or boyfriend is verbally or physically abusive towards you;
- Your family and friends are concerned about your relationship and secretly you agree.

There is no shame in ending a relationship – just be honest and open about it. Trust your instincts, especially if a relationship has been starting to worry you in some way.

CHECK YOUR LEARNING – RELATIONSHIPS

- Explain what is meant by a 'healthy relationship'.
- Identify three qualities that you think are important in a relationship and explain what each one involves.
- Explain how each of these qualities is important in healthy relationships with family, friends and dating partners.
- What are some of the signs that a relationship may not be a healthy one?

PROBLEMS WITH RELATIONSHIPS

What advice would you give in the following situations?

"Sometimes my brother makes me so mad, I could kill him!"

Jack's problem

My brother is only a couple of years younger than me, but he really does my head in. Whenever my mates come round, he always hangs around making stupid remarks. He thinks he's funny, but it's just embarrassing. When we go out, he tries to tag along. Mum says I should try and get on with him, but it's not my fault he's a loser and doesn't have any friends of his own!

"I'm not ready for the kind of relationship my girlfriend wants…"

Brendan's problem

I really like being with my girlfriend but just lately she's started to get too serious. She says she loves me and that we should prove our love to each other by having sex. I just want a bit of fun and I don't want to get too involved with anyone at the moment – after all, we are only 14! Maybe I should finish with her…

"My best friend tells me what to do all the time..."

Gail's problem

My best friend Julie is really popular; she's very pretty and her parents spoil her and buy her lots of nice things. When we go out, it's always where she wants to go – usually because some boy she fancies will be there. Sometimes she even tells me what to wear, just so she can make sure she looks better than me. If I hang around with other girls, she gets in a huff. I don't want to fall out with her as we have been best friends since Primary School.

"My older sister got into trouble, now I'm treated like a baby!"

Ciara's problem

You wouldn't think I am nearly sixteen, the way my parents treat me. I'm not allowed to stay out later than 10:30pm, and my parents always check where I am going and who else will be there. My older sister has left home now – she's in her 20s – but when she was my age she used to hang out with a bad crowd. They would drink in the park and one night the police brought her home drunk. She was sleeping around as well. Now my parents expect me to be the same and they don't let me do anything. It's not fair – I'm not like my sister at all!

evaluation

Evaluate some of the characteristics of a healthy relationship.

....

EXAM FOCUS

In the first two chapters we have practised demonstrating your knowledge and understanding. The next exam skill is to show that you can apply your knowledge and understanding.

The following question tests this skill:

(a) Name one quality that contributes to a healthy relationship.

[1 mark]

(b) Explain one reason why a relationship which is based on physical attraction may not last.

[2 marks]

(c) Explain one reason why parents should encourage their children to be independent.

[2 marks]

Question taken from CCEA's GCSE LLW Modular Specimen Assessment Materials for first teaching September 2009

To gain full marks for (b) and (c) you must write a detailed explanation, for example:

'Physical attraction is only one aspect of a relationship. A couple should have a strong bond based on trust, understanding and commitment if a relationship is to last.'

Try answering part (c).

TIME

1 hour 30 mi

INSTRUCTI

Write your Ce
Answer **all six**

INFORMATIO

The total mark f
Quality of writte
Figures in bracke
question or part q

DVICE TO CA

u are advised to
mination time.

ach

Chapter four
RECOGNISING, ASSESSING AND MANAGING RISK

CHAPTER SUMMARY

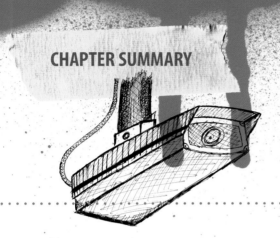

In this chapter you will be studying:

- **What is meant by risk-taking behaviour.**
- **The positives and negatives of taking risks.**
- **Why some young people take dangerous risks.**
- **How to manage risk-taking behaviour.**

WHAT IS RISK-TAKING BEHAVIOUR?

TEENAGERS – OUT OF CONTROL!

This often seems to be the message put across by the media. Newspaper headlines often shout about risk-taking teenagers who cause trouble for other people – stealing cars, driving recklessly and committing acts of vandalism. It seems that some teenagers are almost addicted to taking risks, engaging in dangerous, anti-social behaviour from a young age. People are so wary of teenagers nowadays that if there are more than two of them, and they are wearing hoodies, they are

sometimes banned from shopping centres! The media often focuses on the damage young people do to themselves through risky sexual behaviour and by abusing alcohol and other drugs. Popular television shows often seem to reinforce the idea that many teenagers today are on a course of self-destruction. In reality, the vast majority of teenagers are responsible young people who do not behave in this way.

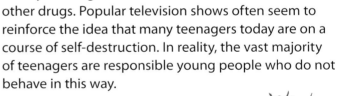

ACTIVITY

Your local newspaper recently ran an article describing young people as "a menace, and a drain on society" . Write an email to the paper explaining your point of view.

POSITIVE AND NEGATIVE RISK-TAKING

Taking risks is a part of life. A person who decided to avoid all risky behaviour would probably never get out of bed all day, as everything we do involves some risk. When a young person becomes a teenager, they will probably become more independent – parents and carers allow more freedom and give greater

responsibility. Increased independence means you have more choices to make for yourself – and that means more risks. This level of risk-taking can be a positive experience as it involves being out on your own more, choosing your own friends and trying new activities.

Positive risk-taking can involve taking on a challenge, such as auditioning for the school play or taking up a new sport. There is a level of risk involved as you may well be in a difficult or unfamiliar situation, and there is always the possibility of failure. However, this level of risk-taking can be a rewarding experience. People need to take risks in order to work towards their goals and the sense of achievement from doing this successfully can bring increased self-esteem.

Some of the deadly consequences of negative risk-taking are:

- Drugs overdose
- Car accidents caused by reckless driving
- Stabbing – if someone takes the risk of carrying a knife.

A sensible approach to taking risks involves thinking about the consequences. This does not mean scaring yourself and refusing to do anything new, but learning how to evaluate risks and make the right choices. If an activity can only bring harm to yourself and others, then it should be avoided.

Some activities do not involve a high degree of risk unless they are carried out to extremes, such as sunbathing or dieting. In situations such as these it is important to keep risks to a minimum by making sensible decisions. However, there is no safe environment for taking negative risks such as driving a stolen car recklessly or abusing drugs.

Negative risk-taking involves behaviour which is usually seen as destructive, anti-social and highly unlikely to have any positive effects. The person who behaves in this way will be putting themselves, or other people, at risk. This could involve both emotional and physical damage. Most of the time, negative risk-taking does not result in the people involved being fatally wounded, but the possibility is always there.

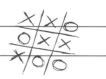

Assessing Risk.

- Working in groups of about 4 or 5, look at the scenarios below.

- For each scenario, consider the potential risks to;
  - yourself
  - others
  - property

- Give each scenario a risk rating from 1–10 (where 1 is low risk and 10 is high risk)

- Finally, decide which scenarios involve positive risk, and which involve negative risk.

- Record your conclusions in a table like the one below:

	RISK TO YOURSELF	RISK TO OTHERS	RISK TO PROPERTY	RISK RATING	POSITIVE OR NEGATIVE?
Having unprotected sex					
Skydiving					
Getting a lift home on the back of a friend's scooter					
Binge drinking in the park					
Rock climbing					
Talking to online friends in a chat room					
A day at the beach sunbathing					
Taking Ecstasy at a party					
Vandalising a bus shelter					
Auditioning for the school play					

CRIME AND ANTI-SOCIAL BEHAVIOUR

Breaking the law and being anti-social in the community involves negative risk and negative consequences, for both the person involved and local residents.

Anti-social behaviour includes such things as:
- Drinking in the street
- Rowdy, noisy and 'yobbish' behaviour in public
- Setting off fireworks late at night
- Stealing cars and racing them in the neighbourhood
- Buying or dealing drugs on the street

Anti-social behaviour can ruin people's lives and lead to whole areas feeling unsafe, even though some of these activities may not be seen as serious crimes.

54

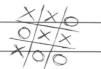
Search online or in newspapers to find stories about vandalism and anti-social behaviour damaging people's lives.

NEWS ITEM

FATAL CRASH FRIENDS 'WERE WARNED'

Four friends who died when the stolen car they were in crashed into a chip shop and exploded had been warned to stop joyriding, an inquest has heard.

Thomas Tilleard, 15, Robert Lyn, 16, Craig James, 17, and James McClusky, 21, died in the crash in Laisterdyke, Bradford, in December 2008.

The Subaru car they were in was being pursued by police when it crashed. Craig and Thomas's mothers told the Bradford inquest they had told their sons to stop stealing cars.

Police used fire extinguishers in an attempt to save them, after the explosion, which was caused when a gas main cracked in the chip shop on Killinghall Road.

Family statements read out at the inquest revealed the young men had a history of car theft.

Linda Tilleard, mother of Thomas, said the last time she saw her son was hours before the crash when he came to her house to get something to eat. She said: "Craig and Robert had acted as lookouts while Thomas ate because the police had been looking for him in relation to a previous car theft.

"I spoke to Craig. He told me they had stolen a Subaru motor car.

"I replied to him, saying: 'Keep out of the cars, you will get yourselves killed.'

"I had been telling them all that for weeks."

Dr Elizabeth Lim, a pathologist, told the inquest that death in all cases would have been almost instantaneous because of the severity of their injuries, which were caused by blunt impact. PC Paul Smith said he spotted the Subaru and began to follow the car but the next time he saw it was when it had crashed and was in a "ball of flames".
The hearing continues.

Story from BBC NEWS Published: 2010/02/16 14:57:45 GMT
Source: http://news.bbc.co.uk/go/pr/fr/-/1/hi/england/bradford/8518402.stm

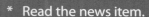
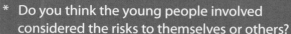

DISCUSSION
* Read the news item.
* Do you think the young people involved considered the risks to themselves or others?
* What advice would you have given them?

Research shows that many young people break the law at some stage. While this might simply mean dodging a bus or train fare, or trying to see an 18-certified film, crime is never acceptable. Some of the most common crimes involving young people are shoplifting, vandalism, car theft and knife crime. Some teenagers go through a phase of shoplifting or vandalism, perhaps because they are bored or short of money. Friends often egg each other on and some risk-taking might begin as a dare. Most teenage crime is committed by groups rather than individuals, so this shows the strong influence of peer pressure.

Some young people might become involved in shoplifting simply because of the thrill of getting away with it, perhaps stealing items they do not need just for the adrenaline rush or to impress others. However, this can easily get out of hand and crime can become a habit. A person who starts to find crime addictive, or is tempted to do it on their own, could be unhappy or suffering from depression and needs to seek help.

Car crime involves a particularly high level of risk-taking and can result in the death of the driver and passengers, or even innocent bystanders. The crime of 'joyriding' usually involves stealing a vehicle, driving it recklessly, perhaps under the influence of alcohol or other drugs, then setting it on fire. Because of the enormous potential for harm and the destructive attitude of those involved, many people regard the name 'joyriding' as totally inappropriate.

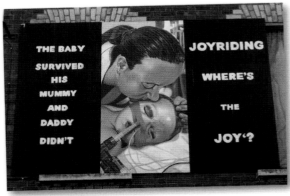

A mural in North Belfast

Vandalism is the deliberate destruction of someone else's property or a public facility. This could include arson (lighting fires), destroying a bus shelter, or spraying graffiti on someone's wall. While a group of bored young people may try to get a buzz from doing this, someone else will suffer.

There is a growing concern about young people carrying weapons, particularly knives. Hospitals report a rise in stab wounds, mostly among young men, showing that knife crime is becoming a serious problem.

Here are some of the reasons why a young person might carry a knife:

- For self-defence
- To feel safe
- To harass or threaten others
- Peer pressure
- To command respect and status

The reality is that people who carry knives are far more likely to be stabbed themselves, perhaps with fatal consequences.

DISCUSSION

Can you think of any other reasons why someone might think carrying a knife was a good idea?

How could you persuade someone that carrying a knife was dangerous?

Taking risks through committing crime is not a way to have fun; both the individual and the whole community can suffer. It's not pleasant to live in an area where public facilities are broken or spray painted. Stealing and wrecking a car is both selfish and cruel, as someone might rely on it for work, or to care for a member of their family. Graffiti is particularly distressing if it involves hateful comments about race, religion or sexuality. Stealing from a small shop where the owners are struggling to make a livelihood might

bring them one step closer to closing down. It is important to consider the effects your actions have on others.

For the person committing these crimes, there are also serious personal consequences to consider. Breaking the law means the possibility of being arrested and perhaps having a criminal record, which could make life difficult in the future. To avoid prosecution, an offender might have to agree to be put under supervision by the police or social services.

ACTIVITY

What are the consequences of negative risk-taking? Work in pairs or small groups and produce a spider diagram. Try to include as many examples as you can.

SEXUAL BEHAVIOUR

The two main physical risks associated with having a 'casual' sexual relationship are:

- An unwanted, unplanned pregnancy
- Catching a sexually transmitted infection (STI)

You do not need to have full sexual intercourse to put yourself at risk of a sexually transmitted infection. Some of the more common STIs can be passed on through intimate touching and skin contact. Although many can be successfully treated, if a sexually transmitted infection is ignored, perhaps through embarrassment or not detecting the symptoms, then the health risks can be very serious.

Sexual health means having respect for your own body with regard to sexual relationships, and showing respect for your partner. It also involves taking care of your body and protecting yourself from diseases and infections.

FACTS ABOUT SEXUALLY TRANSMITTED INFECTIONS

INFECTION	WHAT IS IT?	HOW IS IT PASSED ON?	SYMPTOMS	TREATMENT	LONG TERM PROBLEMS
CHLAMYDIA	A bacterial infection.	Passed through unprotected sexual intercourse or intimate contact.	Pain when passing urine; a white discharge.	Can be successfully cured with a course of antibiotics; sexual activity should be avoided during this time.	Chlamydia can lead to sterility if it is not detected. 50% of men and 80% of women have no symptoms of the infection.
GONORRHOEA	A bacterial infection.	Passed through unprotected sexual intercourse or intimate contact.	A white, yellow or green discharge; frequent need to urinate; pain when urinating; stomach pains.	Can be successfully cured with a single dose of antibiotics; sexual activity should be avoided during this time.	10% of men and 50% of women have no symptoms. If not treated, gonorrhoea can cause infertility and inflammation of the joints.
SYPHILIS	A bacterial infection.	Passed through unprotected sexual intercourse or intimate contact.	Very mild symptoms at first, perhaps a painless sore in the genital area or mouth; this is followed by a rash and flu-type symptoms.	Can be successfully treated with antibiotics; sexual activity should be avoided during this time.	If left untreated, syphilis can lead to heart problems and dementia. If contracted in pregnancy, syphilis can lead to infection of the baby or a still birth, but this is rare in the UK.
GENITAL HERPES	A viral infection.	Passed through unprotected sexual intercourse or intimate contact when there are active blisters.	Painful blisters or sores in the genital area, flu-type symptoms and pain passing urine.	There is no cure although the first attack is usually the most severe. Antiviral drugs can help to make the symptoms less unpleasant.	There will be recurrent attacks of herpes as the virus stays in the body.
TRICHOMONIASIS	Tiny parasites in the woman's vagina or man's urethra.	Passed through unprotected sexual intercourse or intimate contact.	Women – itching and discharge; Men – no symptoms	Can be successfully treated with antibiotics.	Trichomoniasis is not serious; however, it can sometimes be present with gonorrhoea so could be a sign of something more serious.
HIV / AIDS	HIV – Human Immunodeficiency Virus; AIDS – Acquired Immune Deficiency Virus	Passed through unprotected sexual intercourse, where there has been an exchange of body fluids.	There may be no symptoms of HIV for up to 10 years. AIDS sufferers have a seriously weakened immune system.	HIV can be treated, bur not cured, with a combination of at least 3 antiviral drugs taken daily, for life. There is no cure for AIDS but symptoms can be treated.	HIV damages the body's immune system so it cannot fight diseases and infections. HIV leads to AIDS and a premature death.

If the two people having sex are not in a committed relationship, and will have other partners in the future, then the risks of an STI being passed on are much greater. If the couple are young or uncommitted to each other, then any pregnancy is more likely to be unwanted. There is concern about the number of teenage pregnancies in the UK and cases of STIs among young people. It is thought that these are largely due to 'casual sex'.

Even though there is lots of information available about contraceptives, perhaps through a school's sex education programme, many young people are either not using them or are not using them correctly. It is also worth remembering that no contraceptive gives 100% protection against either an STI or pregnancy. They can considerably lower the chance of this happening, but it must be remembered that there is always a risk involved.

Teenage sexual relationships are therefore a high-risk activity, and this is without even considering that there may be drugs or alcohol involved. Drugs and alcohol can lower a person's inhibitions, cloud their judgement and make it less likely that contraceptives will be used correctly, if at all.

Having a sexual relationship at a young age can put emotional health at risk. There is no such thing as 'casual' sex, as having a sexual relationship involves an intimate connection with another person. The end of a relationship can cause a lot more trauma if there has been this level of intimacy.

Taking risks with sexual behaviour can have life-long consequences. You could get a potentially fatal disease, for which there is currently no cure, or becoming a parent a long time before you feel ready for this responsibility.

SEX EDUCATION

There is clearly a need for accurate, honest and open discussion on sexual issues with young people to try and minimise the risks involved. This could take place at home or at school, but there is disagreement as to the best way to do this. There are broadly three different approaches:

Comprehensive sex education – This involves explicit information being given about contraception, relationships and sexuality. This would include advice about where to obtain contraceptives and how to use them correctly. This approach takes the view that, if young people are going to be sexually active, then they should be properly informed about the risks and how to minimise them.

The abstinence approach – This means to abstain from sex; in other words, to remain celibate and not have sex until married. The only way to be certain of avoiding an unwanted pregnancy or STI is to keep all sexual activity for marriage. With this approach, there is no information given to young people about contraception.

The 'abstinence plus' approach – Young people are encouraged not to feel pressured into a relationship they are not ready for. Waiting to have sex – at least until in a committed adult relationship – is the best option. It is okay to say no. However, this approach recognises that some young people will be sexually active and that there is a need for information to be given on safe sexual relationships.

LOVEFORLIFE
informing choice

This is a programme now operating in over 50% of post-primary schools in Northern Ireland. It could be described as adopting the 'abstinence plus' approach. Love for Life was founded by Richard Barr, a GP from Craigavon. The following information is taken from their website:

Our Vision:
To influence change within society so that young people have a healthy respect for themselves, relationships and sex.

Love for Life is a project that supports young people and their carers in the area of Relationships and Sexuality Education. We at Love for Life are committed to the task of empowering young people through supporting their personal development. We believe that young people can make healthy choices for their future if they are adequately equipped to do so.

Love for Life recognises the need for local communities to be resourced and equipped to deal with and actively challenge the pressures young people face to engage in early sexual activity and other risk-taking behaviours.

Love for Life offers four age-appropriate programmes at Post Primary level: Who's Choosing (Year 9), Icebergs and Babies (Year 11), Dating and Mating (Year 12), The Sex Factor (Years 13–14). Our Relationships and Sexuality Education programmes are challenging and engaging, providing a media rich, interactive learning experience, that allows opportunity for on-going personal reflection for pupils on their attitudes and choices around relationships and sex.

Visit **www.loveforlife.org.uk** for more information.

DISCUSSION
Consider the following questions in pairs or small groups:

- Which of the three approaches to sex education is closest to your own experience?
- Which approach do you think is likely to be the most effective in reducing the risks of teenage sexual activity?
- Imagine you are the parent of a young teenager. What attitudes would you want your child to have towards sex?

STATISTICS
Not all young people are sexually active. Precise numbers are difficult to obtain, as some people like to exaggerate their sexual behaviour. Others may be unwilling to admit to a sexual relationship, particularly if they are under-age. However, recent figures suggest that 25% of young women and 30% of young men have had sex under the age of sixteen. This suggests that sexually active young people are very much in the minority.

CHECK YOUR LEARNING

- Explain how taking risks can be a positive experience.
- Give examples of how anti-social behaviour can cause the whole community to suffer.
- What are some of the negative risks associated with unprotected sex and casual sex?
- Give examples of crimes committed by some young people. What risks are involved?

DRUGS AND ALCOHOL

The topic of substance abuse was discussed in Chapter One as part of living a healthy lifestyle. Here is a summary of the reasons why using drugs and alcohol can be harmful:

- Street drugs are illegal; this means that there is the possibility of a criminal record for possessing them.
- Street drugs have not been prepared under strict conditions, nor do they come with dosage instructions. Taking illegal drugs is a gamble: you do not know how pure they are, or what they have been mixed with. For some users, taking this risk has fatal consequences.
- Alcohol is a poison, so there is always some level of risk attached to drinking alcohol. However, it is particularly dangerous for young people to drink, as alcohol can cause even more damage to body organs that are still growing and developing, such as the liver.
- Drugs, including alcohol, alter a person's mood, perhaps lowering their inhibitions or causing them to behave in a foolish or reckless way. Alcohol has a stronger effect on a young person's body, making them more likely to lose control on far fewer drinks.
- These substances are addictive; occasional or recreational use can quickly turn into dependency and become a serious addiction.

There is a direct link between using drugs and alcohol and risk-taking behaviour. By using these substances, a young person is taking a risk which could be fatal. Also, taking drugs and drinking alcohol make it more likely that a person will become involved in other risky behaviour as well.

Many young people drink or use other drugs in the company of others, away from the home. This means there is a greater chance of negative peer pressure, as they can be encouraged to go beyond their own personal limits. Alcohol and some other drugs can cause a person to feel very relaxed and lose their inhibitions, doing things they would not normally do. Drinking alcohol affects a person's judgement and this could lead to them doing something stupid or embarrassing that they regret the next day. Someone could be pressured into having sex more easily if they have drunk alcohol, and would be far less likely to even think about using contraceptives. A group of young people who have been drinking or taking drugs are more likely to commit a crime – they are not going to consider the consequences of their actions. Drinking alcohol can make a person aggressive and more likely to get into a fight. This can be particularly dangerous if anyone involved is carrying a weapon, such as a knife.

Binge drinking is when people go out with the intention of getting as drunk as they can as fast as they can. The increase in a binge-drinking attitude to alcohol, particularly among young people, is a cause for concern.

As there is a direct link between drinking alcohol and risk-taking behaviour, the risks will be greater if a person drinks more. Binge drinking among young people usually takes place in the company of others, where there is considerable peer pressure to drink large quantities – perhaps it may even be part of a game to down a drink in one go.

Drinking large quantities very quickly is dangerous – the body cannot cope. This can cause:

Vomiting – The stomach lining becomes irritated and the person becomes very sick as the body attempts to get rid of the alcohol.

Unconsciousness – In large quantities, alcohol is a depressant, so a person may become unconscious as the result of a serious binge. This can cause considerable health problems and also risks to personal safety. Who is going to look after you if you end up in this state, and how will you get home?

Alcohol poisoning – A person who becomes unconscious through binge drinking may need to be taken to hospital, as there is a risk of liver damage caused by alcohol poisoning. This may involve an unpleasant and distressing stomach pump. If your liver stops working, you die.

Solvent abuse carries a particularly high level of risk. Inhaling aerosol products, lighter fluid or other volatile substances, can cause instant death from asphyxiation, as the body's airways go into spasm. Sometimes solvent abuse causes vomiting or unconsciousness – or both. If this happens there is the possibility of death through choking. Statistics show that, in the UK, 60 people a year die the first time they abuse solvents – they don't get the chance to realise their mistake

NEWS ITEM

BINGE DRINKING IN STRABANE NORTHERN IRELAND

A personal view by a peer educator.

In Strabane binge drinking is usually more frequent with teenagers than adults. However, many adults in Strabane are also guilty of binge drinking. I believe young people are influenced by peer pressure which leads to a sociable drink then to binge drinking. This is more frequent in teenage boys than girls but is increasing among young females in my experience. Binge drinking is responsible for ample problems such as; domestic violence, deterioration of family relationships, underage sex, teenage pregnancies, fights and vandalism. Young people in Strabane drink for a variety of reasons such as; boredom, to have a good time, it is seen as the norm and it is easy to get.

In Strabane some youth start drinking at a very early age. Some as young as twelve. This is common amongst both males and females in the local area. It is easy for young people to gain access to local bars or get a 'carryout' and gather at one of the local drinking spots to get 'wasted'. Questions need to be asked; why are these young people being served drink? Where do they get the money for alcohol? And why does no one know they're drunk when they get home?

There have been complaints from members of the public about too much drinking on the streets of Strabane. At the weekend if you went down town sober the behaviour of those out on a 'bender' would be very intimidating. High spirits often get out of control and lead to violence and mayhem. In the last few years the local papers have tried to highlight these issues and have written various stories concerning underage drinking, binge drinking and the high consumption of alcohol in Strabane. There have been more assaults and violence than ever before and most of it is down to drink. More worrying have been the increasingly reported cases of date rape.

Taken from EDGES MAGAZINE issue 41, April 2005
Source: http://www.users.globalnet.co.uk/~edges/online/issue41/p11.htm

FACTS AND FIGURES FROM THE PUBLIC HEALTH AGENCY Press Release 19.10.05

Research reveals worrying trends in underage drinking in Northern Ireland.

Summary of key findings:

- Experimentation starts early – the average age for the first drink is around 11 years old.

- Traditionally boys were more likely than girls to experiment with alcohol and to get drunk but gender differences are now disappearing – 59% of boys had tried a drink compared with 58% of girls in 2003.

- Some 24% of young people in the 2003 survey were classed as regular drinkers (drinking at least once a month) indicating drinking had become part of their lifestyle.

- Many young people who drink say that they drink to get drunk.

- There is a trend towards more risky patterns of drinking among young people over the last 10 years.

- The relationship between drinking behaviour and other risk behaviours, such as smoking experimentation, drug and solvent experimentation and sexual behaviour, is strongly significant.

Source: http://www.healthpromotionagency.org.uk/Work/Publicrelations/PressReleases/
temperancereport05.htm

Read the statistics on underage drinking and the personal view on binge drinking.

Write a letter

- Imagine you are the chairperson of a local community group.
- Write a letter to the editor of a local newspaper giving your concerns over teenage drinking and rising levels of crime in your area.
- Suggest what could be done to improve the situation.

Role play

A meeting has been arranged at a local community centre to discuss concerns over teenage drinking in the area and increasing levels of anti-social behaviour.

The following people are present:

- A 15-year-old, currently under an Anti-Social Behaviour Order (ASBO)
- The parent / carer of the young person
- A police officer
- A community worker
- A concerned local resident

- Work in groups of five and give each person a role to play.
- Discuss the problem with each group member keeping to their role.
- Report back to the rest of the class with your conclusions.

SUICIDE AND SELF-HARM

Self-harm is when someone deliberately inflicts pain or injury on themselves, perhaps by hitting, cutting, or burning themselves. Self-poisoning, by taking an overdose, is also an example of self-harm. Though not all people who self-harm are suicidal, there is a close link between self-harm and suicide. Often the decision to attempt suicide is made quickly; it is a reaction to desperate unhappiness and feelings of helplessness rather a calculated plan to die.

Page 34 lists organisations that exist to help people who are self harming or suicidal.

Here are some reasons given by young people about why they self-harm:

"It helps me find relief from a really bad situation; I feel in control."

"I feel it is the only way to get my own back."

"Everything goes wrong and it's all my fault; I need to punish myself."

"It's the only way I can get anyone to notice me."

"Sometimes I feel so angry I think I'll explode; it helps me calm down."

Although self-harm and attempted suicide are extremely risky, they are sometimes regarded as being different to risk-taking behaviour, as described in the rest of this chapter. This is because the motivation is different. It would be rare for a young person to self-harm just to get the buzz of an adrenaline rush, to impress their peer group, or out of boredom. While other risk-taking behaviour is anti-social, self-harm is rarely intended to hurt others. It is often a cry for help. Some young people might deliberately inflict harm on themselves because they are deeply unhappy or cannot cope with everyday life. They feel that this is the only effective way of drawing attention to their problems, but it is important to talk to someone.

MAKING CHOICES, AVOIDING RISKS

There are some activities where the level of risk involved depends on making the right decisions. They can be relatively harmless if guidelines are followed or sensible choices made. Here are some examples:

SUNBATHING

You might wonder how this could be a high risk activity in Northern Ireland! However, there are two important points to keep in mind:

1. The ultra violet rays from the sun that reach earth are called UVA and UVB. In the summer, the UVB rays which cause the skin to be tanned are much stronger. UV rays can still do damage even if it doesn't look like a sunny day. UV can cause damage to the skin and premature aging.

If you do a lot of outdoor activities, it is sensible to wear a sunscreen whatever the weather.

2. 'Binge sunbathing' is especially dangerous. Many people spend hours in the sun as soon as there is a warm, sunny day – or they go on holiday to a much hotter climate and bake on the beach all day so they can go home with a tan. Short, intense exposure to the sun is especially dangerous and can double the chance of getting a malignant melanoma.

Melanoma is the most fatal kind of skin cancer and is caused by exposure to the sun's UVB rays. A sign of melanoma is a small mark on the skin, like a mole, which increases in size, changes shape or colour or starts to bleed. In the UK, there are 9,500 melanoma cases each year and over 2,000 deaths.

Australia has one of the highest rates of skin cancer in the world. In 1981 a health campaign began called 'SLIP-SLOP-SLAP'. The seagull mascot, Sid, encouraged people to slip on a T-shirt, slop on some sunscreen and slap on a hat before going out in the sun, in order to protect against skin cancer. The campaign was hugely successful, and cases of skin cancer in Australia were reduced significantly. Sid and the campaign have now been updated to include seek shade and slide on sunglasses.

Permission for use of the Sid the Seagull image granted by SunSmart, Cancer Council Victoria.

DISCUSSION

Why do people want to be tanned?

In the past, having pale skin was considered to be attractive. Some cultures where darker skin is more usual seem to value paleness and there are even cosmetics to make the skin lighter. An increasing number of men are now using dangerous tanning methods because of the example of some celebrities.

Do you think we should just accept the natural colour of our skin?

DIETING

The importance of eating a balanced diet as part of a healthy lifestyle was discussed in chapter one. There is nothing wrong with following a diet, particularly if some weight needs to be lost for health reasons. However, extreme dieting, or 'crash diets' can be very harmful and even fatal. Surviving on a very low calorie diet in an attempt to lose as much weight as quickly as possible is not recommended by doctors, and can severely damage your health. One of the characteristics of an eating disorder, such as anorexia, is that sufferers will often starve themselves for long periods of time. A person who decides to go on a crash diet may not necessarily have an eating disorder, but sometimes this near-starvation approach to food can lead to a long-term problem with diet.

What are the risks of extreme dieting?

A person on a crash diet may experience intense hunger, stomach cramps, bad temper, low energy and tiredness, depression and constant cravings for food.

There may be very rapid weight loss. This is not a good thing, as it is not only excess fat that is lost, but muscle and water as well. Extreme diets can weaken the body and trigger an underlying health issue, such as a heart condition or problem with the kidneys.

In extreme cases where the body is seriously starved of sugar, a chemical reaction takes place as the body is forced to try and make its own energy. This can lead to dangerously high levels of a chemical called ketone being produced, which can be fatal.

DISCUSSION

- Why do people take the risks of extreme dieting?
- Do they have a poor self-image?
- Do you think the media is also responsible?
- Can you think of any other reasons?

TATTOOS AND BODY PIERCING

Tattoos, piercing and other forms of body art are becoming increasingly popular. There is little risk of infection from tattooists or body piercing studios in the UK as strict health and safety laws have to be followed. However, any activity that involves cutting or piercing the skin can be potentially dangerous, and not everyone is tattooed or pierced by qualified staff, or in the UK. Think very carefully about who you are asking to cut or pierce your body and whether you can be sure their hygiene standards are excellent. There is a risk of HIV infection, or other diseases carried in the blood, such as hepatitis, if instruments contaminated with blood are not sterilised properly. Even if the piercing conditions are

hygienic, there is still a risk of infection later on. Nose piercings can be difficult to keep clean as they heal and can easily become infected. It is particularly risky to have the naval pierced as any infection can affect the internal organs, such as the liver. The other issue to think about very carefully is whether you will still like your body art in 10 or 20 years time. How will it look on your 80-year-old body?

PERSONAL SAFETY WHEN GOING OUT

It does not matter whether you live in a city, town or rural area – you need to take responsibility for your own safety when out and about. This does not mean being so fearful that you cannot enjoy yourself, but it does mean being smart and making sensible choices.

Some ways to keep yourself safe and avoid risks:

- Always let someone at home know where you are going and who you will be with.

- Do not walk home alone at night – make sure you have a lift arranged, enough money for a taxi home, or stay in the company of your friends.

- Stick to your own alcohol limits and do not accept drinks from strangers.

- If you are at a party and a lot of people are drinking heavily, it might be better to leave.

- If leaving is not possible, stay with people you know and trust. Keep an eye on your own drink so you know exactly what you are drinking and in what quantities.

- When you are out never leave your drink unattended. This is to prevent it being 'spiked' either with drugs or more alcohol than you are comfortable with.

ROHYPNOL – THE 'DATE RAPE' DRUG

Rape is always a serious crime, even if the victim is on a date with her attacker, and he will not accept that when she says "No" to sex that she means it.

A date rape drug is any drug that is used to assist in a sexual assault. Alcohol can be used in this way, perhaps to spike a drink so the victim becomes drunk and is not in control of what is happening to her. The drug rohypnol (which has the common slang names of 'roofies' and 'forget me') is often associated with date rape. This drug is sometimes used medically when a high level of sedation is needed. If abused, and slipped unnoticed into someone's drink, it can cause a person to be completely unaware of what is happening and can cause total memory loss. A girl who has had her drink spiked with rohypnol can be raped and remember nothing about it – or her abuser.

Rohypnol has no taste and was originally colourless until the manufacturers, concerned about its abuse for date rape, coloured it blue. However, in dark coloured drinks (like cola) or in a dimly-lit club, it may be difficult to detect.

YOUNG DRIVERS

Most young drivers are responsible and only a minority could be considered dangerous. Irresponsible drivers are not only risking their own lives, but the lives of others. It causes problems when young drivers try to impress their friends or get a thrill from driving dangerously. Some young people – especially men – like to show off when driving, so they are less safe when there are passengers in the car. The passengers themselves can also be a problem, particularly if they have been drinking and

are encouraging the driver to take risks. It is illegal to use a mobile phone when driving, but some people ignore this. Young drivers in particular are more likely to use a mobile phone when driving and this greatly increases the chance of having an accident.

If you get into a car with a driver who you don't think is going to drive safely, particularly if he or she has been drinking or taking drugs, then you are taking a huge risk which could result in serious injury or death.

The following facts are from the website of the AA:

- 135 teenage drivers were killed on the roads in 2007, another 1000 were seriously injured and 10,000 slightly injured.

- One in five drivers has an accident in the first year of driving.

- Nearly 15,000 teenage passengers were casualties in road accidents in 2006. 167 were killed. Many of these would have been in cars driven by teenage drivers.

- Teenage females of driving age are 33% more likely to be killed or seriously injured while travelling as passengers than as drivers. Males of the same age are 50% more likely to be killed as drivers than passengers.

- Young drink drivers are hugely more at risk than those who are older.

- Of the 9040 drink drive accidents in 2007, over 3000 involve a driver under 25.

- Against a national average of 25 drink drive accidents per 100,000 registered drivers, young drivers record over 70.

Source: http://www.theaa.com/public_affairs/reports/younger-people-christmas.html

DISCUSSION

Discuss the statistics above. Do any of them surprise you? Why do you think young drivers are more likely to be involved in accidents than older drivers?

THE INTERNET

Some of the issues concerning Internet use and negative pressure on young people have been discussed in Chapter Two. When considering risky behaviour and sensible choices to minimise harm, there are some important considerations.

Sexual predators use the Internet, particularly chat rooms and social networking sites, to make contact with young people. One of the attractions of the Internet is that it is anonymous, but this is also a reason why it can be so dangerous for a young person. Sexual predators can use the Internet to stalk their victims, usually posing as a child or young person themselves. This is why it is particularly risky to meet up with someone you chat to online and don't know in the real world. You should never do this.

Social networking sites, like Bebo and Facebook, are being used by teenagers to post information about their risk-taking behaviour, such as sexual relationships, substance abuse or violence. The danger is that potentially harmful behaviour is seen as something to boast about. Other people may want to copy what they have read about.

CHECK YOUR LEARNING

Assess the risks involved with each of the following:

- under-age drinking
- solvent abuse

For each of the following, give one potential risk and one way in which this risk can be minimised:

- using the Internet for social networking
- sunbathing
- getting a tattoo or piercing
- going out to a party

WHY DO YOUNG PEOPLE TAKE NEGATIVE RISKS?

Boredom: Facing challenges, taking risks, feeling excitement – these are all part of living a life that is interesting and fulfilling. Some people, however, feel that their lives are dull and boring. They may turn to risk-taking behaviour for the thrill it gives them.

Attention seeking: Some young people feel lonely and isolated from their peer group and may also feel that parents, carers and teachers do not have any time for them. Taking part in a risky or anti-social activity can be a way to try to get attention.

Peer pressure: Some people are more likely to be affected by peer pressure than others. For some young people, just being with a group of friends makes them more likely to take risks than if they were on their own. Peer pressure creates feelings of wanting to impress others and a desire to be accepted by the group. These feelings are more important than considerations of personal safety, harm to others or being in trouble with the police.

Addicted to the adrenaline rush: Adrenaline is a hormone which is produced by the body in situations of danger or stress. It causes the heart rate to increase, blood vessels to contract and airways to dilate. These feelings can be very intense and are described as an adrenaline rush. Some people take part in extreme sports like bungee jumping as they love the feelings of exhilaration that come from an adrenaline rush. However, getting enjoyment from an anti-social or harmful activity is wrong. There are better ways to do something exciting.

Influence of drugs: Drugs, such as alcohol can make a person more reckless and therefore more likely to take risks in any situation – crime, sexual activity or when driving. After a person has sobered up, they may really regret what they have done, as they would never have acted in such a way without the drugs or alcohol.

Financial gain: Some people take risks by committing crimes, perhaps shoplifting or breaking and entering into someone's house. The motivation to steal could be a mixture of greed, wanting to impress others and doing it for the thrill of taking risks.

MANAGING RISK

HOW TO AVOID RISK-TAKING BEHAVIOUR

Self-evaluation of risk – This means considering the consequences of doing something and thinking about future outcomes rather than short-term pleasure. A person tempted to take part in risky or anti-social behaviour should ask themselves:

• Could this activity harm me physically or emotionally?
• What could be the long term effects on my health?
• Could it harm others or the community?
• Is this activity against the law?
• Could I get a criminal record which could affect my future?
• Will taking part in this activity damage my relationships (with parents or carers, for example).

Anti-social behaviour has no positive benefits. It causes nothing but upset and anger, puts the young person in danger and at risk of having a criminal record, and does nothing for his or her self-esteem.

Resist negative peer pressure – Remember that everyone has the right to be treated with respect. This means that no one should be bullied or forced into doing something they are unhappy with,

particularly if this activity carries risks to personal well-being or safety. An effective way to deal with negative pressure is to be assertive – this means being firm about your personal limits without being aggressive. Say 'no' firmly and stick to your decision; true friends should respect your feelings. If the crowd you hang out with seems to be spending more and more time in petty crime such as shoplifting, graffiti or vandalism then maybe it is time to find new friends! Learning to be assertive means knowing when to stand up for yourself and your beliefs. It is an important step towards becoming a responsible adult.

Consider alternative activities – There are plenty of constructive channels for taking risks, such as a sport or outdoor activity. Mountain biking, rock climbing, canoeing or playing a team sport could be a positive way of getting an adrenaline rush. Even though some of these activities might be considered potentially dangerous, taking part with qualified instructors can greatly reduce the risks involved. Of course, not everyone enjoys doing the same thing and some people hate the thought of sport or outdoor pursuits. However, there are plenty of constructive activities – something creative, or perhaps some voluntary work or a part time job.

POSITIVE INFLUENCES ON BEHAVIOUR

Parents and carers – As children grow up, they learn how to behave from those around them. With very young children, parents and carers will have the greatest impact on behaviour. As the child gets older, other influences start to become important, such as friends, school and society. However, family support and guidance for a young person remains crucial. Research has shown that young people with strong family support are more likely to resist negative peer pressure.

Teaching by example is important, as young people tend to copy what their parents do, rather than what they say. This is especially important when it comes to having a healthy attitude towards alcohol. Parents can set a good example by being honest about the health risks of alcohol.

School – Through the school curriculum, or perhaps through visiting speakers, the message about the dangers of negative risk-taking can be underlined. The idea that anti-social activities are 'fun' or a 'bit of a laugh' can be challenged through discussion and activities in class.

The media – Although the media can have a very negative influence on teenagers' behaviour, there are some campaigns which are trying to bring about a positive change in attitude. One example has been a campaign to deter knife crime and the growing trend among some young people to carry a knife. High profile posters have appeared on bill boards and buses.

The same techniques have been used to reinforce sensible attitudes towards alcohol, and also to encourage parents to take more responsibility for their children's behaviour. A recent campaign focussed on the importance of getting home safely, by using text messages: WR R U? and RU HOME YET?

evaluation

Evaluate how peer pressure can have both a positive and negative effect on a young person.

....

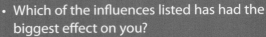

DISCUSSION

- Which of the influences listed has had the biggest effect on you?
- What other positive influences do you think there are in your life?

FIND OUT MORE...

Visit the following websites:
www.knifecrimes.org
www.ntk.org.uk (no to knives)
www.alcoholparentsupport.com
www.publichealth.hscni.net
www.drinkaware.co.uk

QUIZ: CAN YOU HANDLE PEER PRESSURE?

Do you make decisions for yourself or are you easily influenced by your friends?

For each situation, decide which response is closest to how you would act. Give yourself the following scores:

0 = Never

1 = Sometimes; perhaps I might do this

2 = Fairly often; I would be quite likely to do this

3 = Always; I do it all the time

1. Do you buy clothes you don't really like so you can look the same as your friends?

2. If you were at a party and some of the people there were drinking too much, would you join in?

3. Would you steal sweets from a local shop because your friends were doing it?

4. Would you ever lie to your parents about who you were meeting or where you were going?

5. If someone offered you a cigarette, would you take one just to 'fit in'?

6. Would you change your hairstyle because your friend told you to?

7. Have you ever done something you know to be wrong because you thought it would make you popular?

8. Would you tell lies to a teacher in school to get your friend out of trouble?

9. Your best friend starts picking on someone. Would you join in to please your friend?

10. Would you join a club or team you are not interested in because your friend wants you to?

11. Your friend asks for your help to cheat in an exam. Would you do it?

12. In a dating relationship, do you go with what your boyfriend/girlfriend expects when it comes to sexual activity?

13. Has a friend ever persuaded you to do something that you have later regretted?

14. Have you ever done anything illegal to impress others?

15. Have you ever taken a risk with your safety because your friends have encouraged you?

How did you score?

0 – 15: You are an independent thinker and are not likely to be influenced by negative peer pressure. You have a clear sense of what is right and wrong. Keep it up!

16 – 30: You like to fit in with others, even if this does mean occasionally doing something you might regret. On the whole, you know your own standards and manage to keep to them most of the time.

31 – 45: You are too far easily influenced by other people. Sometimes it is good to consider other people's feelings, but not if you are persuaded to do something dangerous or illegal. Start thinking for yourself!

EXAM FOCUS

In this chapter we are continuing with the skill of applying your knowledge and understanding.

The following question will give you further practice at this:

(a) Name one benefit of taking risks.

[1 mark]

(b) Explain one reason why a young person might deliberately put their health and safety at risk.

[2 marks]

(c) Explain one reason why Internet safety is important for young people.

[2 marks]

To gain full marks for (b) and (c) you must write a detailed explanation, for example:

'Some young people can feel under pressure to fit in with their peer group. If their friends are binge drinking or vandalising property, a young person might join in without thinking about the consequences, deliberately putting their health and safety at risk.'

Try answering part (c).

oklet provided.

4 and 5.
cate the marks awarded

stion in allocating the ava

exam

Chapter five

UNDERSTANDING THE ROLES AND RESPONSIBILITIES OF PARENTING

CHAPTER SUMMARY

In this chapter you will be studying:

- **The challenges which young parents may have to face.**
- **Some of the emotional issues involved in coping with parenthood.**
- **Financial considerations.**
- **Education and career prospects for young parents.**

THE CHALLENGES FACED BY YOUNG PARENTS

It is not easy to be a parent – in fact, parenthood could be described as the hardest challenge a person may ever have to face! If the parents-to-be are teenagers with no financial security and probably still living at home, then this can make a difficult task even more daunting. Being a parent is a full-time, demanding job – with very little time off, especially in the first few years. Teenage parents have to cope with the demands of a child, perhaps on their own, as well as sort out their own careers and plans for the future. Many teenage pregnancies are unplanned and so this means there are only a few months to come to terms with the huge changes that having a child will bring. A young person about to become a parent may well feel that their life is no longer their own and that things will never be the same again. There are a lot of challenges to be faced – emotional issues, financial matters and career prospects.

TEENAGE PREGNANCY

- The UK has the highest teenage birth and abortion rates in Western Europe.
- The UK rates of teenage births are seven times those in the Netherlands, double those in France and more than twice those in Germany.
- Groups of young people who are more likely to become teenage parents include those who are: in or leaving care, homeless, underachieving at school, children of teenage parents, involved in crime or living in areas with higher social deprivation.
- Young women living in socially disadvantaged areas are less likely to opt for an abortion if they get pregnant.
- In Northern Ireland, there were 1,405 teenage births in 2007.
- In 2007, an estimated 235 teenage girls travelled from Northern Ireland to England where they can legally have an abortion.
- In Northern Ireland, the government aims to reduce the number of births to teenage mothers under 17 years of age. The target is to have a 25% reduction by 2013.

Figures taken from fpa (The Family Planning Association). Factsheet available on their website: http://www.fpa.org.uk/Information/Factsheets/teenagepregnancy

WHY DO TEENAGERS BECOME PREGNANT?

The obvious answer to this question is that some young people are sexually active. However, they are either not using any contraceptives, not using them every time, or else not using them correctly. Sometimes drugs or alcoholic drink are the reason why precautions against an unwanted pregnancy are overlooked.

There are also myths passed around about getting pregnant – for example, that you cannot get pregnant the first time you have sex. You can! Myths such as these can lead to some uninformed young people having unprotected sex.

Statistically, some young people are more likely than others to become teenage parents due to social factors. A teenage girl who has been excluded from school, or left school early, perhaps with no qualifications, is more likely to become pregnant. Engaging in early sexual relationships or even deliberately becoming a mother can seem like a good option if she feels she has no other role in life. This is one of the reasons why teenage pregnancy rates tend to be higher in areas where many people are poor or unemployed. On the other hand, young people who see a good future ahead of themselves, in either further education or employment, are more likely to try to avoid an unplanned pregnancy.

Teenagers who have been sexually abused when they were younger are more likely to suffer from low self-esteem and self-confidence. These feelings can lead to inappropriate relationships where there is a greater risk of a young girl becoming pregnant, or a boy becoming a father.

EMOTIONAL ISSUES

WHAT DOES BEING A RESPONSIBLE PARENT INVOLVE?

Young mothers and fathers face many different tasks, all requiring a variety of personal skills and qualities. Here are some of the main ones – but the list is probably endless!

- Providing for the material needs of a child and seeing to his or her physical demands, such as the need for food and clothing. The family home should be a safe environment, a place of comfort, warmth and happiness.

- Giving love, care and time to a child. This will involve encouraging any interests and skills the child might have, and providing opportunities for social development. Children should grow up knowing they are loved and valued.

- Listening to your children and trying to create an atmosphere where they can talk about anything that is worrying them.

- Showing respect for privacy – this is particularly important for teenagers.

- Being responsible for the behaviour of your children and having the right to discipline them within reason. Firm and consistent boundaries should be set.

- Ensuring that your children go to school until they are at least 16.

- Deciding which religion, if any, you want your children to be brought up in. Parents should make sure that their children learn morals and values which will help them to be good citizens.

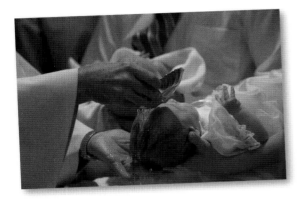

- Never mistreating or harming a child through shaking, hitting or neglect.

- Protecting your child from abuse. Child abuse takes many forms – emotional, mental, physical and sexual; a responsible parent will do all they can to make sure their child does not suffer abuse.

- Not showing favouritism – one child in the family should not be made to feel inadequate or that they can never compare to a successful sibling.

- Looking after a child's health and well-being and asking for help if there are problems. This may involve making sure a sick child is taken to a doctor, or seeking medical help for an injury.

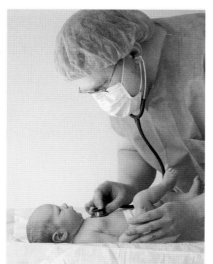

- Encouraging responsibility, by letting children make decisions for themselves and encouraging them to learn from the experience.

- Being a role model – Children need to have a good example which they can follow.

It is therefore a huge responsibility to be a parent. While nobody expects parents to be perfect, they owe it to their children to try and do their best for them. This can be very difficult, especially when children become parents themselves and have very little emotional or financial support.

DISCUSSION
What do you think are the most important qualities in a parent?

AM I READY TO BE A PARENT?
When facing an unplanned pregnancy, it is important for couples to consider the options available.

Continue with the pregnancy, and remain together. The mother has the support of the baby's father. This might involve getting married if the couple are over 16 years of age, or they might decide to live together and both take responsibility for the child's upbringing.

Continue with the pregnancy as a single parent. This could be because the girl is unsure who the father is, or does not want to name him. Sometimes the father does not want to play a role in the child's life, and the mother would raise the child without his support.

Continue with the pregnancy and consider an adoption.

Some people, faced with an unplanned pregnancy, decide that this is the best option for them. Adoption is a legal agreement, arranged by an adoption agency or health board, and involves placing the child with adoptive parents. This is a permanent arrangement and the birth parents will no longer have any rights or responsibilities towards the child. When an adopted child reaches 18 years of age, he or she has the right to contact their birth mother, if they wish to do so.

Consider an abortion.

This can be a very difficult decision to make. Abortion is a very emotional subject with many people having strong views about whether it is right or wrong. For many people, abortion is simply not an option as it goes against their religious or moral beliefs.

It is also important to remember that abortion is not legal in Northern Ireland unless there is a serious medical consideration. The only option would be to travel to England, where abortion is legal. Two doctors must agree that this is the best course of action and the pregnancy must not be more advanced than 24 weeks. This would involve paying for travel and the fee for a private clinic to carry out the abortion.

Abortion is not a quick and easy solution to the problem of an unwanted pregnancy, as it can lead to long-term feelings of guilt and depression. Having an abortion can also cause physical problems. These include:

- An increased chance of breast cancer, or cancer of the cervix, uterus or liver
- A haemorrhage or infection
- Perforation of the uterus
- Complications in a future pregnancy and birth.

DISCUSSION

Read the quotes below from two women who had abortions:

"The day I found out I was pregnant I booked into an abortion clinic. I had no intention of being a mother at 19 years of age. For me, it was a lifestyle choice and I have no regrets."

"I had the abortion a long time ago. I'm married now with two children, but I still think about my first baby, the one I destroyed. Sometimes I look at Lucy and Jack and I wonder what their older brother or sister would have been like… I don't think I'll ever forget the abortion."

Discuss both views.

HOW DOES PREGNANCY AFFECT THE BODY?

When a woman carries a growing baby inside her body for nine months, it affects how she is feeling physically, especially as the baby gets bigger. However, there are very significant hormonal changes going on as well, and these also have an effect on the mother's physical and emotional health.

Some side effects of pregnancy might include:

Changes to the skin – Pregnancy can cause the skin to appear darker overall or for patches to appear on the forehead, cheeks and neck. Pregnancy hormones can sometimes cause acne, or trigger increased sensitivity and irritation so eczema becomes a problem.

Mood swings and depression – These are usually caused by hormonal changes in the body and are perfectly natural. However, if a young mother-to-be is scared and anxious about her pregnancy then feelings of depression need to be taken seriously. Perhaps she feels she cannot cope with being a mother and is afraid to tell anyone, or is keeping the pregnancy a secret. If this is the case then she needs advice and support.

Nausea and sickness – Feeling sick and vomiting are quite common, especially early on in pregnancy. Other side effects may include heartburn, backache, feelings of tiredness, swollen legs and varicose veins.

As many of these changes are caused by hormones, they usually stop being a problem once the baby is born.

THE HEALTH RISKS OF TEENAGE PREGNANCY

There are always health risks attached to being pregnant, but these are much greater for a teenage girl or a mature woman nearing the end of her fertile life. There are potential risks to both physical and mental health.

Physical health

Some of the health problems which may be faced by a pregnant young woman include high blood pressure, anaemia and a serious condition called eclampsia.

With a planned pregnancy, doctors recommend that nutritional supplements are taken before becoming pregnant, as well as for the duration of pregnancy. However, as many teenage pregnancies are unplanned, this often does not happen. Some young girls will keep their pregnancy a secret for as long as they can for fear of other people's disapproval. They will not be getting the vital medical support that they need in the first few months of pregnancy. A pregnant teenager needs to be especially careful about her nutrition, exercise, health care and rest, as her own body is still growing. If a girl becomes pregnant when her body is not fully grown, there is an increased risk of the following:

Damage to her spine and pelvic bones – It is not just the delivery of the baby which can cause problems. Carrying the baby, especially in the last stages of pregnancy, can put tremendous strain on the body.

Premature birth – A premature baby is one that is born too early. Some premature babies as young as 22 weeks can survive with intensive medical care, but many do die. Those that do survive can have long-term mental and physical disabilities.

Low birth weight baby – A low birth weight baby is one weighing under five and a half pounds. These babies are more likely to be born with serious birth defects, as their major organs (brain, lungs and heart) are not fully developed. A low birth weight baby has a much higher chance of dying in early infancy than a normal weight baby.

A prolonged or difficult labour – This may be due to the small physical size of the mother and can cause complications for both her and the baby.

The younger the mother is, then the greater the chance of health risks and complications during pregnancy and birth.

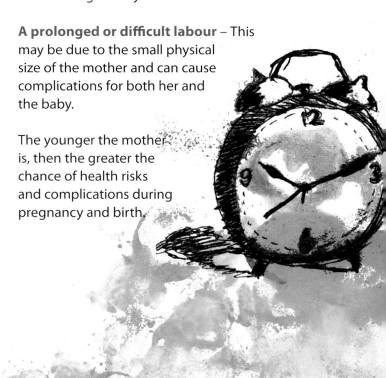

Mental health

About half of all mothers suffer from the 'baby blues' after giving birth. This may leave them feeling easily upset and a bit low for a week or two as the body settles down following pregnancy. About 10% of older mothers and 40% of teenage mothers suffer from a more serious condition called postnatal depression. While this normally passes with time, very young mothers can have mental health problems for up to three years after the birth.

Teenage fathers can also have mental health problems. The increased pressure of responsibility and uncertainty about the future can cause stress, depression and anxiety. Many young fathers require emotional support.

SOCIAL PROBLEMS OF BEING A TEENAGE PARENT

There are a number of social problems associated with being a teenage parent that can have an impact on both the young person and the child they are raising. Here are some examples:

Pressure on relationships – Relationships that start during teenage years have a greater chance of breaking down than relationships that begin later on. If a young couple have decided to marry or live together because of an unplanned pregnancy, then statistics suggest that they will no longer be together by the time the child is a year old.

If a young person who is still living at home has a baby then this can put enormous pressure on relationships with the rest of the family. Parents may experience shock, anger and sometimes feelings of guilt or responsibility. They may also have a sense of disappointment that the career dreams they had for their daughter are now unlikely to happen. Younger brothers and sisters living at home may think it unfair that they are expected to help out with child-minding

duties. If a young parent is living at home with a baby, then the rest of the family needs to be very understanding and supportive for the arrangement to work well.

Restrictions on social life – For the teenage mother-to-be, these restrictions begin long before the baby is born. A healthy lifestyle is essential during pregnancy and this includes absolutely no smoking, drinking or taking drugs. The blood supply of the unborn baby is linked directly to that of the mother through the umbilical cord, so any poisons pass straight to the baby. Smoking during pregnancy can cause damage to the baby's lungs and slows down growth and development. Passive smoking is also dangerous, so it is not just the mother who has to be careful, but her partner as well.

There is no safe amount of alcohol during pregnancy, for women of any age. The only way to avoid the risk of damage to the unborn baby is not to drink at all.

Some STIs can be passed to the baby, and these can cause complications at birth. If a pregnant girl remains sexually active, especially with different partners, then it is still essential to use contraceptives to help prevent the risk of infection.

Even if a young mother is happy to follow a healthy and responsible lifestyle, there will still be restrictions on the mother's social life, particularly as the pregnancy progresses. Once the baby is born, child care arrangements have to be considered before planning to go out with friends. Teenage parents can miss out on an important part of their own childhood because they are busy taking care of their baby. Some young parents may find that they no longer have anything in common with friends as their lives have changed so much.

Social stigma – We might like to think that we live in a tolerant society, but often this is not the case. It can be distressing and hurtful to be on the receiving end of another person's prejudice. Some people might assume that a young girl who becomes pregnant is both promiscuous and irresponsible. Future boyfriends may think that, because a girl has already had a baby, she will always be willing to have sex. A future partner may feel uncertain about taking on the responsibility of a child. Having to deal with other people's attitudes could be difficult during an already stressful time.

Feelings of isolation and exclusion – There is concern that teenage parents who care for a child on their own can become excluded from society. They may not be able to continue with their education, find suitable employment or take part in any training schemes.

PROBLEMS FOR THE CHILD

Research has shown that:

- Children born to very young mothers are less likely to receive proper nutrition and healthcare.

- There is also an increased risk of abuse and neglect. Children of teenage parents are more likely to be admitted to hospital because of an illness or accident than the children of older parents.

- The children of young, unmarried mothers are more likely to become parents themselves when they are teenagers.

DISCUSSION

Why do you think that the child of a very young mother is more likely to suffer from these problems?

TEENAGE FATHERS

In the case of an unplanned pregnancy, the young father often receives blame, but little in the way of counselling and support. Sometimes it is assumed that young fathers will want nothing to do with the pregnancy or the baby, but this is not always the case. The father also has rights and responsibilities.

Ultimately, it is the choice of the young woman whether to continue the pregnancy or have an abortion. Either decision may be difficult for the young father to accept, especially if he has not been consulted. Some couples may continue to support each other and make important decisions about the future together.

DISCUSSION

Read the following dialogue:

NIALL: I don't think it's fair that fathers have no right to decide what happens to their baby.

GRACE: Of course it's fair! If a teenage boy gets a girl pregnant, then he never wants anything to do with the baby anyway. Why should he have a say?

NIALL: Well, if I was in this situation, I wouldn't like to think that my girlfriend could get an abortion without even telling me!

GRACE: Why shouldn't she? It's the girl who has to carry the baby for nine months and then risks wrecking her career. An unplanned pregnancy doesn't mess up a boy's GCSEs does it?

Discuss the following *(in mixed groups if possible)*:

- Which of the two views do you agree with?

- How might a young father feel during a pregnancy?

- How might a young father feel if the mother decides to have an abortion?

- How might a young father feel if the mother decides to keep the baby?

- Do you think teenage fathers should have more rights?

NEWS ITEM

BABY FACED BOY ALFIE PATTEN IS FATHER AT 13

Boy dad Alfie Patten yesterday admitted he does not know how much nappies cost – but said: "I think it's a lot."

Baby-faced Alfie, who is 13 but looks more like eight, became a father four days ago when his girlfriend Chantelle Steadman gave birth to 7lb 3oz Maisie Roxanne. He told how he and Chantelle, 15, decided against an abortion after discovering she was pregnant. The shy lad, whose voice has not yet broken, said: "I thought it would be good to have a baby. I didn't think about how we would afford it. I don't really get pocket money. My dad sometimes gives me £10."

Alfie, who is just 4ft tall, added: "When my mum found out, I thought I was going to get in trouble. We wanted to have the baby but were worried how people would react. I didn't know what it would be like to be a dad. I will be good, though, and care for it."

Alfie's story, broken exclusively by The Sun today has sparked a huge political storm with Tory leader David Cameron saying: "When I saw these pictures this morning, I just thought how worrying that in Britain today children are having children. I hope that somehow these children grow up into responsible parents but the truth is parenthood is just not something they should be thinking about right now."

Source: http://www.thesun.co.uk/sol/homepage/news/article2233878.ece#ixzz0lIMJkPb3

ACTIVITIES

Read the news item.

1. Discuss the following issues in small groups:
   - What is your view on this newspaper article?
   - Do you think 13 is too young to be a father?
   - What positives are there in this situation?
   - What could be done to try and prevent children from becoming parents?

2. Write a letter to the editor of the newspaper giving your view on young teenage parents.

HELP FOR YOUNG MOTHERS – BARNARDO'S SAMS PROJECT

The children's charity Barnardo's runs a project in Northern Ireland called SAMs – School Age Mothers. The following is taken from their website:

"We work with young parents in their own communities to identify the issues which are relevant to them and then we work out the best way to support them to deal with these issues. Usually these are things which cause stress or difficulties for the young parents eg. money, relationships, housing, and behaviour problems. Sometimes they are about helping young parents to understand the systems they have to deal with on a day-to-day basis eg. social welfare, education, social services or the medical services.

We usually work with young people in groups as we believe that this is the best way of ensuring peer support and of reducing the isolation and loneliness that many parents feel. Sometimes the work is very informal, for example in a drop-in setting; sometimes it is more formal, for example in a project for school-aged mothers or in other structured programmes.

Structured programmes will focus on those things that the parents tell us they are most interested in or would benefit most from, ranging from child development, personal development, health, relationship issues or skills development.

We have developed practical resources such as toy and book libraries in two communities and also produced practical guides written for young people by young parents about what it's like to become a parent when you're young, and highlighting local supports and services.

Young Parents' Network, in partnership with Education and Library Boards, Health & Social Services Trust and community groups have developed a programme for young women of compulsory school age who are pregnant or who are parents. The School Age Mothers (SAMs) Project is community based and provides education, personal development and antenatal support in order to help the young woman continue her education during and after her pregnancy. We know from our work with many young mums across Northern Ireland that unless they receive practical and specific support, eg. child care and tuition, at this time in their lives they are likely to leave school early, miss opportunities to sit exams, find it very hard to get a decent job and to be stuck in the poverty trap for many years. Their children are also likely to lose out in the long term if the mums don't get this support and encouragement.

© Barnardo's 2010
Source: http://www.barnardos.org.uk/youngparentsbelfast/microsite_young_parents_belfast_what_we_do.htm

ACTIVITY

Read the information on SAMs.

- List the problems and worries faced by a young single mother.

- For each, give an example of how this project aims to help.

FINANCIAL ISSUES

HOW MUCH DOES IT COST TO HAVE A BABY?

The following figures are based on the average amounts spent by parents. Some people will economise and spend less, perhaps by buying second-hand equipment or borrowing expensive items from family and friends. However, some parents will spend much more!

- Before the baby is born, around £1,600 will be spent on essentials such as pram, changing and feeding equipment, baby monitor and clothes. This figure does not include decorating the nursery, which can cost an extra £1,000 or more.

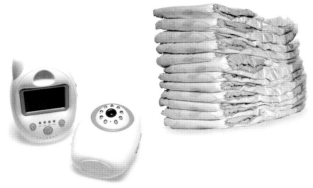

- An additional £8,500 will be spent in the baby's first year. The money might be spent on nappies, infant milk formula, baby food, clothes, toys, cot, baby walker, safety gates, play pen and many other items.

- It is estimated that raising a child from birth until 21 years of age currently costs around £200,000. This figure covers essential items, such as food and clothes – it does not include luxuries, holidays or the cost of further education.

Therefore, raising a child is not just a commitment in terms of time and energy; it is an enormous financial commitment as well.

PAYMENTS AND BENEFITS

The government provides some financial help for parents and parents-to-be. This is aimed at helping with the cost of some essential items and encouraging expectant mothers to stay healthy. These are some of the benefits available:

Free prescriptions and NHS dental treatment – All women are entitled to this during pregnancy and for 12 months after the birth of the baby.

Health in Pregnancy Grant – This is a one-off payment to help with extra costs in the last months of pregnancy, for example, spending money on healthy and nutritious food. A mother-to-be can get the grant if she is at least 25 weeks pregnant and has been given health advice from a midwife or doctor about staying healthy during pregnancy.

Child benefit – This is paid to all people who are bringing up children and it is not affected by a family's income or savings. Single parents may also be entitled to additional help as well as the basic child benefit.

Social Fund Maternity Grant – If a young mother lives with her parents and they are claiming Child Tax Credit, then they may be able to claim this grant for their daughter and her baby. Parents can also claim vouchers for free milk, fruit and vegetables for a pregnant girl living at home.

Educational Maintenance Allowance (EMA) – A young parent who stays in education and is between 16-18 years old may be able to claim this weekly cash allowance.

OTHER CONSIDERATIONS

If a teenage girl finds herself raising a child on her own, as a single parent, there are some important issues to consider which will affect how much money is available:

Where will I live? The best option might be to continue living at home even though a lot of patience and understanding will be needed to prevent strained relationships. A single mother under the age of 18 years will not normally be able to get rented accommodation. However, if living at home is impossible, then hostel accommodation might be a possibility, provided by a voluntary organisation. In some cases foster care for a young mother and her baby might be provided by social services. If a teenage mother decides to live with the father of the baby, she will need to be over 16 years of age and have her parents' consent. At 18 years old she no longer requires her parents' consent.

Will my family support me? Family support can be crucial, regardless of whether the young mother is living at home or not. Looking after a baby or young child is very demanding and time consuming. It can be very difficult finding any time to work at a part-time job, do some studying or even to have some leisure time. Childminders can be very expensive and this may be impossible for someone on a tight budget. Family members can show their support by helping to look after the baby from time to time. Another important way for the family to show their support is by trying to accept the situation and not be judgemental.

What help can I expect from the baby's father? This will vary considerably, depending on the strength of the relationship. It may be that the two young people involved want very little to do with each other. Even if the father does not want to play an active part in the life of his child, he may still have a legal obligation to give financial support. The amount of maintenance money to be paid by the father depends on his financial circumstances. This is calculated by the Child Support Agency (CSA) and a court order may be issued if the father refuses to pay. However, if the father is still at school or studying full time and has no income, then by law he does not have to pay anything.

LARA'S STORY

Lara was a few weeks away from her sixteenth birthday when she discovered she was pregnant. She was due to take her GCSE exams in a few months time. Five years later, with son Ruari now in Nursery School, Lara is trying to finish her education and plan her future. In the following interview she talks about her experiences:

What has been the most difficult time for you?
The early days, most definitely. I remember trying to pluck up the courage to tell my mum. I just couldn't do it. It was about three weeks later that I eventually told her, and during that time I felt dreadful. In the end, Mum was okay about it, but Dad was so disappointed with me. That was really difficult, the feeling that I'd let him down and spoilt all the high hopes he had for me. Living at home after Ruari was born also put quite a strain on family relationships. I don't think anyone likes to be woken at three in the morning by a screaming baby!

How did other people react to the pregnancy?
Well my boyfriend dumped me! Not that we were ever really much of an item to begin with…well, he just wasn't ready to be a father. We should never have had sex in the first place. Some of my friends just drifted away, as we no longer seemed to have anything in common. That was hard; I missed not having girlfriends to chat and gossip with. I still see my best friend from school, although we're not as close as we were. Sometimes it's the reactions from strangers which can be difficult. When I was out pushing Ruari in his buggy, I often felt people were giving me disapproving looks as if they were thinking, "That's awful, she's a mother already at her age!"

You mention school. What about your GCSEs?
A disaster! Well, perhaps not that bad. I did get five passes in the end, but not the grades I was expecting. I was pregnant at the time, and although my school was very supportive, I was constantly feeling tired and sick, which didn't help me do my best.

Do you still live at home?
Not now; I was able to get a flat once I turned 18, and that made relationships a bit easier with my family. Some of my friends think it's really cool to have your own place to live, but it can be very lonely at times especially when you only have a small child for company. I also don't have the money to do it up the way I'd really like it, or to buy nice things.

What are you doing now?
Now that Ruari has started Nursery I have been able to enrol at my local college. I am doing a Certificate in Childcare. It's not what I would have chosen for a career, but this sort of work should fit in well with having Ruari to look after.

What about the future?
I really don't know. I'd like to move to a house with a garden for Ruari to play in, but money is very tight so that is not an option at the moment. I'd like to get out more often and have some social life, but that's not usually possible either!

Finally, do you have any regrets?
I have a lot of regrets, but the one thing I have never regretted was going ahead and having Ruari. He's a great little boy and makes it all seem worthwhile. For me, abortion was never an option. I do worry sometimes that Ruari is missing out on things that other children have.

DISCUSSION

From reading this interview, what regrets do you think Lara might have?

CAREER PROSPECTS

EDUCATION

Studying and taking exams is never easy – especially when pregnant, or when looking after a baby. However, it is possible to be successful and there is a lot that can be achieved through a determined attitude and a supportive school.

By law, a young person has to remain in school until 16 years of age, so a pupil cannot be excluded from school because of pregnancy. However, if a young person cannot attend school because of the birth of the baby, then an alternative must be provided. This is usually through home tuition, with up to 10 hours a week of teaching provided. While this does not replace school, it does help to prevent a pupil getting too far behind with lessons. A supportive school may be able to work out a reduced or altered timetable coming up to the birth, and will be understanding about time taken off school for hospital and doctor's appointments.

If the baby is due around the same time as exams, special arrangements may have to be made. These could include the girl being given a room to herself, with her own supervisor, and being allowed to take breaks during an exam.

After the baby is born, and once the young parents have reached 16 years of age, the decision will have to be made about continuing with school or education. A key consideration will be 'Who will look after the baby?' This might depend on support from other members of the family. Some colleges might have a crèche, to encourage single mothers to continue with their education.

A young father who intends to support his new family will have to consider very carefully what the best course of action is. Leaving school and finding work will bring in money, but in the long term continuing with his education might be the most responsible thing to do.

FUTURE CAREER PLANS

It is during teenage years that most young people start to make plans for their future careers – making subject choices for GCSEs, deciding whether to go on to Sixth Form study or get a job, or perhaps considering college or university. Having a baby during this time is going to change a young person's priorities and may make some of these choices impossible.

Statistics show that teenage mothers are more likely to finish their education early and live on a lower income than young women who do not have a child to care for. The reduced income is the result of having to live on benefits or do a part-time or unskilled job.

Even though career plans may be difficult for teenage parents, many young people are determined to make a success of their education and have a promising career even though they have a baby to care for as well. It is not easy, but it can be done!

DISCUSSION

Sandra and Brendan go to the same school. They are in Year 14 and will be taking their A2 exams in a few months time. As they have been dating for about eighteen months, they feel quite committed to each other and hope their relationship will continue next year when both expect to go to university. Sandra discovers she is about three months pregnant; both she and Brendan are very upset as this is not what they had planned!

- What are the problems facing Sandra and Brendan?
- What are the choices that each has to make?
- What factors will influence their choices?
- Write your own ending for this scenario.

CHECK YOUR LEARNING

- Explain why some young people are more likely than others to become parents when they are teenagers.
- List the five most important qualities that you think a good parent should have.
- If a teenage couple are faced with an unplanned pregnancy, what are their alternatives if they decide not to bring up the baby themselves?
- How can pregnancy cause health risks to:
  - A teenage mother?
  - The baby she is carrying?
- List some of the social problems often associated with teenage pregnancy.
- What practical help is available for young, single parents?

AVOIDING AN UNPLANNED PREGNANCY

Pregnancy occurs when the male sperm meets the female egg and fertilisation takes place. Contraceptives help prevent pregnancy by preventing the sperm and egg coming into contact with each other. There are many different types of contraceptive available but they work in two main ways:

- A barrier is created between the sperm and egg
- Hormonal changes take place in the woman's body to prevent release of an egg (ovulation).

All contraceptives can be obtained free on the NHS through a Family Planning clinic or GP. Some types of contraceptive can be bought in chemists, garages and supermarkets.

Important to remember...
Contraceptives can be very effective, but only if they are used correctly. If you forget to take a pill at the correct time or do not put a condom on properly, then protection is considerably reduced.

Barrier contraception, such as a condom, prevents body fluids from one person entering the body of another. As well as preventing pregnancy, these types of contraception will help to stop the spread of STIs. Hormonal methods of contraception do not offer this protection.

Young teenage girls have a much higher rate of failure with the pill, especially within the first six months of using it. The body needs to have settled into a regular cycle of monthly periods for the pill to be most effective.

CONCLUSION

Most people would agree that having a child at a very young age is not desirable. So what can be done to try and reduce the likelihood of teenagers becoming parents? The UK has the highest teen pregnancy rate in Europe – seven times as high as the Netherlands. Perhaps the UK could learn a lot from other countries about sex education and teenager's attitudes to relationships.

NEWS ITEM

In Britain the average teenager loses his or her virginity at 16 – more than a year before the Dutch average of 17.7 years. About 93 per cent of young people in the Netherlands use contraception, compared with 53 per cent in Britain.

A study of teenagers in both countries found that while boys and girls in the Netherlands gave "love and commitment" as the main reason for losing their virginity, boys in Britain cited peer pressure and physical attraction.

Source: http://women.timesonline.co.uk/tol/life_and_style/women/the_way_we_live/article5208865.ece

Info Box

Some countries with a low rate of teenage pregnancy have these features:

- Good sex education in schools, where issues about relationships are discussed in an open and honest way. In Denmark, sex education is usually started at around 9 years of age while in the Netherlands contraception and sexuality are discussed in over half of primary schools. Sex education starts at 6 years of age in Norway.

- Teenagers have access to contraceptives, and information about their use is freely available. Sweden has around 150 youth clinics providing contraceptives and advice on their use. The Netherlands has the highest use of contraceptives among young people in the world.

- In the home, there is an open and relaxed attitude between young people and parents when talking about sex and relationships.

- Young people are encouraged to feel assertive about their relationships and do not feel forced into a sexual relationship before they are ready.

DISCUSSION

Look at the info box and the news item.

- How do you think the factors described could reduce the number of teenage pregnancies?

- What other factors might affect the number of teenage pregnancies?

- The number of teenage pregnancies in the UK is rising steadily. Why do you think this is?

evaluation

Evaluate the impact an unplanned pregnancy can have on a young couple.

EXAM FOCUS

Some questions testing the application of knowledge and understanding will need longer answers.

The following question will give you practice at this:

(a) Explain some of the challenges faced by teenage parents.

[6 marks]

(b) Explain how teenage pregnancy can be damaging to:

(i) Physical health [2 marks]

(ii) Family relationships [2 marks]

You will see that part (a) is worth 6 marks. To gain high marks in part (a) you need to write clearly and develop your ideas in a paragraph.

INSTR

Write y
Answer

INFOR

The total
Quality o
Figures in
question

ADVICE

You are ad
examinatio

ded to each

ailable

Chapter six

DEVELOPING COMPETENCE AS DISCERNING CONSUMERS

CHAPTER SUMMARY

In this chapter you will be studying:

- **What is meant by managing a budget.**
- **The advantages and disadvantages of using cash or credit.**
- **How to make sensible choices as a consumer.**
- **Some of the problems associated with debt.**

MANAGING A BUDGET

WHAT IS A BUDGET?

If you have pocket money, do you spend it on going to the cinema with friends or saving up for a new computer game? If you earned more money by doing a few extra jobs at home, could you afford to do both? If a friend's birthday is coming soon you might have to save your money to buy a present. Making decisions like these involve your budget.

A budget is a plan for spending and saving. It involves asking yourself:

- How much money do I have available?
- How much do I expect to earn or be given?
- What should I spend my money on?

Some of these expenses will be essential while others will not. Having a budget is all about prioritising how your money should be spent, so you can meet obligations to other people and use your money for your own benefit.

A budget can be either short term or long term. A short term budget will involve managing your finances (your money) effectively for the next week or month ahead, perhaps making sure that you have money to spend if you go out with friends at the weekend. A long term budget might involve saving for a summer holiday or an expensive item, such as a new computer.

NEEDS AND WANTS

When making a budget, it is very important to consider the difference between needs and wants. A need is something necessary for survival, such as food, clothing and shelter.

A want is something we would like to have, such as a new mobile phone or a better car. These items can enhance a person's life but they are not absolutely necessary.

Some items can be both a need and a want. For example, food is needed for survival, but a meal in a very expensive restaurant could be considered a want rather than a need. Clothes are essential, but they do not have to be the latest fashion or have a designer label; these clothes are wants not needs.

A person's lifestyle or the society in which they live can influence whether an item is a need or a want. Many people would consider a computer to be an essential part of their life. However, in some parts of the developing world, electricity is regarded as a luxury.

WHY HAVE A BUDGET?

Effective money management can make all the difference between being in control of your life or feeling stressed out and worried about how you are going to cope. Developing good habits with money is all about getting into a routine, like healthy eating or taking regular exercise. It might seem boring at first, but in the end will help you to make the most of life.

There are many advantages to having a budget. It can help you:

Spend money wisely – A budget can show you exactly where your money goes. This can help you to decide whether money is being well spent or wasted and whether you need to change what you are spending most money on.

Achieve money goals – Money is a tool that can help you reach a certain goal, whether it is to own the latest phone or pay off the mortgage. A budget can help you to use this tool effectively so that goals are reached.

Stay out of debt – Having a budget is all about planning ahead, being aware of what expenses are coming up and making sure that there is money available to cover them. A person who plans their spending carefully is more likely to avoid getting into debt as they will not be forced into having to borrow money to meet essential expenses.

Save money – Even on a very small income, it is possible to save money with careful budgeting. Savings can help with money management, when unforeseen expenses occur that have not been budgeted for. Putting savings in certain bank accounts means they can grow by gaining interest.

Identify needs and wants – A budget can help you to sort out your spending priorities so that needs are met before money is spent on wants.

ACTIVITIES

1. Create a pie chart showing what you spend money on each month.

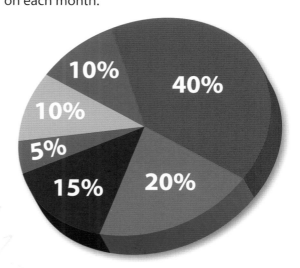

2. Work out a budget for yourself that balances your monthly income with your expenses and also allows you to save for something you really want to buy.

THE FAMILY BUDGET

It is especially important for a family to have a budget and manage money efficiently. Household income and expenditure can be complicated and everyone in the family will have their own competing needs and wants. There may be disagreement between family members as to what is an essential item

and what should be considered a luxury. In a typical family, there will be short-term expenses to budget for, such as the weekly food bill, and long-term financial commitments. These might include paying the rent or the repayments on a loan for a car.

A family's income may come from the following sources:

Employment – When an employee works for an employer, he or she will get wages in return. In many families, the main income is the salary from the work of one or both parents, either part-time or full-time. Sometimes a young person in the family will be employed and make a contribution to the household expenses.

Self-employment – This means working for yourself in order to earn money. A person who is self-employed may own a business, or offer a service that people pay money for, such as child minding or decorating.

Investments –Some people make an income from their savings. The money is carefully put away, perhaps with a bank or building society, in the hope that more money will be paid back in the future. Some investment schemes will pay out a regular amount of interest while others give a lump sum at the end of the period of investment. The larger the amount of money invested, the more money it may be possible to make. A family struggling to make ends meet would probably not be in a position to have large investments.

Benefits and pensions – There are a variety of government benefits which people are entitled to depending on their circumstances. A person who is unemployed and seeking work may be able to receive a Jobseeker's Allowance and other financial help such as Housing Benefit to help with paying rent.

A family on a low income, even if this is from paid employment, might qualify for Income Support. An ill or dependant member of the family could be entitled to a Disability Living allowance or Attendance Allowance to help with any special care requirements. Parents with school age children may qualify for Child Tax Credit. Elderly members of the family over 65 years of age are entitled to a State Pension.

A family will need to budget its income against outgoing expenses, which will probably be a mixture of needs and wants. If the family's expenditure is less than its income, then the family is saving money. There may be times when the family expenses are more than the money coming in, perhaps because of an unforeseen circumstance such as the car breaking down or repairs to be done to the house. If this becomes a regular occurrence, then the family is in danger of getting into debt.

A family's expenses might include:

Housing – This is probably the largest expenditure in the family budget as it includes paying rent or a mortgage, as well as bills for the maintenance of the house. With a rented property, these bills will probably not be so large since some of the upkeep will be the responsibility of the landlord.

Household bills – Paying for electricity and for fuel to heat the home, such as gas, oil or coal, will take up a large part of the family's income. Other household bills include:

- insurance for the contents of the house and possibly for the house itself if it is owned or being bought;
- repayments on any loans or credit agreements. This will also include monthly credit card payments and any bills from mail order catalogues;
- paying rates to the council – money which goes towards public services such as rubbish collection and recycling;

Food – This includes money spent in the supermarket, which is a large weekly expense for most families. There may also be additional bills for any items that are delivered, such as milk, and money for lunches during the week, perhaps school meals for children in the family.

Clothing – This is another potentially large expense, especially when trying to budget for the clothing that family members want as well as what they need. Sometimes 'luxury' items of clothing or shoes can be given as presents to help with the cost.

Transport – Maintaining a car, or possibly two, can become very expensive. As well as the bills that can be planned for, such as road tax, fuel, insurance and regular servicing, cars can be a source of unexpected expenses from breakdowns and accidents.

Children – The expenses associated with children change as they grow. Babies can be expensive as they need nappies, formula milk and a constant supply of new clothes. Older children may need an expensive school uniform or equipment for a hobby or sport that they enjoy.

Entertainment and holidays – While these can be considered as wants rather than needs, many people expect to have a holiday or money to spend on leisure activities as a reward for working hard the rest of the year. Many families make it a priority to have money available for an annual holiday. Entertainment could include going out, as well as subscriptions to television channels and Internet Service Providers.

Savings – Some families regard savings as important, perhaps to have a 'nest-egg' for retirement, or to help pay for further education for the children.

With a family budget it is important to consider whether income is on a weekly or monthly basis, and how often the bills have to be paid. Some are calculated annually, such as rates, while electricity is quarterly. However, many families find that paying for household expenses by **Direct Debit** can help with budgeting. A set amount is taken from a person's bank account on a regular basis, usually monthly, and so bills do not have to be paid all in one go.

ACTIVITY

Meet the Jacksons – they are quite a large family! They need a fairly big house and car, as there are now seven of them. Mr Jackson is self-employed as a financial advisor, giving advice to his clients about investments and pensions. Mrs Jackson works part time in a local nursery school. This is really convenient as she has 3-year-old Amanda to look after. Then there is 5-year-old Jamie and the twins, 10-year-olds Hannah and Robert. They will be starting secondary school soon. Claire, at 15 years, is the eldest child. Sometimes she finds her younger sisters

▶

and brothers a bit of a pain, but she is hoping to escape from them over the holidays and go on the school trip to France. Finally, Mr Jackson's mother is now staying with the family for a few months as she recovers from a mild heart attack.

- What are the family's main sources of income?
- Make a list of all their possible expenses in a typical month.
- For each family member, give an example of a need and a want.
- Explain why needs and wants may be different for each member of the family.

CHECK YOUR LEARNING

- What is a budget?
- What are some of the advantages of having a budget?
- Use examples to explain the difference between a need and a want.

PAYING CASH OR USING CREDIT?

"I want it now!" The media, particularly television, seems to encourage this attitude with adverts and shopping channels promoting expensive luxury items – all available on credit. Bill boards constantly advertise sales for new furniture or bargains on new cars – usually on a 'buy now pay later' basis.

When, in the past, people would have saved up to buy something, now they are more likely to pay using credit. Whether you want a dream holiday, a computer or a new carpet, you can have it immediately and worry about paying for it at a later date. Buying with credit can have many advantages over using cash – but there is also the potential to overspend and get into debt.

Info Box

What is meant by interest on a loan?
Sometimes a person will lend money as a favour, for example, to a friend or family member, and they will only want the original amount of money paid back to them. However, most loans are made with the intention of earning money for the lender so the borrower has to pay back more than the original amount of the loan. The extra money paid on the loan is called 'interest'.

What is meant by APR?
The letters APR stand for 'Annual Percentage Rate'. This is very important in relation to any loan or credit agreement, as the APR tells you the rate at which you will be charged interest. By law, the APR rate has to be carefully calculated in a standard way so the consumer can easily compare the cost of different loans. Usually, a high APR means that the yearly rate of interest will be high. However, there are also other factors to take into account, such as possible administration fees and a penalty for deciding to pay off the loan early and avoid some of the interest due.

What is meant by 'credit limit'?
A credit card or store card will have a spending limit set on it by the bank or shop issuing the card. If you spend up to your limit, then you cannot use the card until some of the debt is cleared.

What is meant by 'credit rating'?
Nowadays, there is a lot of information held about people in databases. If you have a loan and do not meet some of the repayments, this information is stored electronically and your credit rating is lowered. Now let's say you want another loan in the future. The company you are applying to can access this information and may refuse the loan.

PAYING BY CASH

This is the easiest way to buy things. You simply hand over the money and receive the goods and services that you need! Paying by cash works extremely well for many different transactions, particularly when the amount of money involved is relatively small. However, paying by cash does have serious limitations, especially in an age where we are relying more and more on banks, building societies and plastic cards.

Advantages:
– There is less temptation to overspend and get into debt if you pay by cash rather than using credit.
– Paying by cash is best for small items.
– It can be easier to keep track of your spending and keep to a budget.

Disadvantages
– Paying by cash for expensive items is impractical. People do not usually want to receive thousands of pounds in cash as payment for a new car or extension to the house, for example.
– If cash is lost or stolen it is impossible to replace it.
– Shopping through catalogues or the Internet cannot usually be done through cash payments.
– Many people no longer receive their wages or benefits as cash, so paying cash can be inconvenient.

CREDIT CARD

A credit card allows the card holder to borrow money in order to buy goods and services. The total amount that can be borrowed is determined by the card holder's income and credit rating. Credit cards are often issued by banks and building societies. When a person uses a credit card to make a purchase, the money is not automatically withdrawn from their bank account. At the time, the card provider pays for the purchase. At the end of the month, a statement is sent out, detailing the purchases and informing the card holder how much money is owed. There is the option of paying the outstanding balance immediately, or paying by instalments over a period of time. If a person chooses payments over a long period, they may end up paying more interest. Credit cards are not usually issued to young people under 18 years of age as they are a way of borrowing money.

Advantages:
– Credit cards are a very convenient way to pay, especially for expensive items that you do not want to buy with cash. They can also be safer than cash as a PIN number is needed to use a credit card in a shop.
– As the balance does not have to be paid all at once, many people find them a helpful way to budget.
– Shopping online is becoming increasing popular, and a credit card makes this possible. Many people use the Internet to book their holiday using a credit card, finding greater flexibility and cheaper prices than going to a travel agent.
– Some credit cards allow you to earn 'cash back', depending on how much is spent on the card. Other incentives include reward points which you can convert into shopping vouchers.

Disadvantages:

- Credit cards allow a person to spend more money than they have in the bank, so it can be very tempting to overspend, particularly at Christmas or when on holiday. Later on they get a bill that they cannot afford to pay.
- With a credit card, it is very easy to lose control of what you are spending. If you run out of cash, then you cannot buy anything else. However, with a credit card you can keep on spending up to your credit limit. Credit cards are very easy to use and debts can quickly mount up.
- If just the minimum amount of a credit card bill is paid each month, then the debt can go on for years, maybe even longer than the life of the item you bought.
- Interest has to be paid on any amount of money that is still owed, and if you are late making a payment, then an additional fee is charged on top of the interest.
- If you go over the limit on your card then a penalty charge has to be paid. It can become difficult to control how much is owed.
- Credit cards are all about making money – for the card provider and the retailer but not for the person who owns the card.

DEBIT CARD

A debit card gives direct access to the card holder's account, usually a current or savings account with a bank or building  society. Debit cards are similar to a cheque or cash as the money is taken directly from the bank account, and if there is no money in the account then the transaction is declined.

Advantages:

- A debit card is safer than cash; if it is lost or stolen it cannot be used without a PIN number.
- Many people prefer a debit card to cash as it is more convenient. Debit cards can be used in shops, restaurants and garages, and also for online shopping.
- Debit cards can also be used to withdraw cash from your bank account using the card in a cash machine.
- There is not usually a fee for using a debit card.

Disadvantages:

- Although there is not the same danger of going into debt as there is with a credit card, it is still easy to overspend. Debit cards are very quick and easy to use.
- Even though you are spending money from your account, not money you have borrowed, you could easily waste money on an impulse buy. Perhaps this money should have been left in the bank to cover a Direct Debit for an essential expense!
- As with all cards, it is important to be careful about fraud. The card number should never be written down and care should be taken when using your card that no one sees you type your PIN number at the checkout.

STORE CARD

A store card is a form of credit card. They are issued by a shop and can only be used in that particular store.

Advantages:

- These are the same as for an ordinary credit card. However, store cards often offer more rewards and discounts when you use the card.
- Store cards can be convenient if you do a lot of shopping in one shop and do not want credit facilities anywhere else.

Disadvantages:

- Again, these are the same as for a credit card – but the interest rate could be much higher than for a credit card issued by a bank or building society. These details need to be checked carefully, as shops are in the business of making money!

Work in groups of about four for this activity

SHOP TILL YOU DROP

Your neighbour has had her roof space converted into a bedroom for her 10-year-old child. The new room has a carpet, but nothing else. You have been given a budget of £1,000 to completely furnish the room.

1. Find the items you want on the Internet and in store catalogues.

2. You can pay in three different ways.
   Each method of payment has its own advantages and disadvantages:

• CASH
+ There are no interest rates or hidden charges.

- You can only buy products available locally, and cannot shop online.

• CREDIT CARD
+ You can buy from online stores.

- If you spend over your limit of £500 you will have to pay the difference in cash, plus an extra 10%.

• STORE CARD
+ For every £10 you spend you get £1 extra to spend in the same store.

- If you spend over your limit of £80 you will have to pay the difference in cash, plus an extra 30%.

3. Keep a note of how much you have spent. Remember to take any interest rates into account.

4. Produce a poster for your group showing pictures of what you decide to buy, with details of price and how you paid for the item. Have you managed to keep to your budget?

5. Compare your result with other groups in your class. *Who do you think has created the best room – and kept to the budget?*

A PERSONAL LOAN

A personal loan gives someone the opportunity to borrow a large sum of money from a bank or building society. This could be for many reasons, for example, a car or a major repair to the house. The loan has to be paid back with interest. A loan can be either secured or unsecured. With a secured loan, the borrower provides the lender with a guarantee that the loan will be repaid. If the person borrowing the money owns their home, then this is often used as security. This means that if the repayments on the loan are not made, the bank can sell the borrower's house to recover any money that is owed. An unsecured loan does not require this, but the interest rates might be higher.

Advantages:
– If it is handled sensibly, a personal loan can give help with extra money when it is needed most.
– A personal loan is a relatively fast way to get funds for a special purchase or project, and even large amounts of money can be borrowed.
– The interest rates may be quite competitive, as a large sum of money is often borrowed. It is good to shop around and try to get the best deal.
– With a secured loan, you can generally borrow a larger amount of money and have greater flexibility with the arrangements for paying it back. You can also have access to the money faster, often within 24 hours.

Disadvantages:
– A person may end up regretting the tough repayment schedule; they may realise that they can't afford the repayments that they agreed to. If you cannot make the repayments when they are due, you may face a penalty. If the loan is secured, you may even lose your home.
– If you cannot repay the loan, your credit rating will be affected. This means you may not be able to borrow money in the future.
– However, if you decide that you can afford to pay off the loan early, and want to avoid interest payments,

you may be charged a fee for doing this. Always remember that the financial institutions that give loans want to make as much money as possible!

evaluation

Evaluate the benefits of using cards rather than cash when paying for goods and services.

CHECK YOUR LEARNING

- Explain how a credit card differs from a debit card.
- Why is a credit card more likely to lead to problems with debt than a debit card?
- Why might someone take out a personal loan?
- Explain the difference between an unsecured and secured loan.
- What are the advantages and disadvantages of paying by cash?

CONSUMER CHOICES

As consumers, we have a lot of choices to make about what to buy and how to pay for products and services. It is important for a buyer to think about what is best for them and not to be influenced by the latest offer. Through advertising there is tremendous pressure on people to spend their money. If you have to keep to a budget, which most of us do, then it is important to make the right choice.

Here are some key questions to consider:

SHOULD I CONSIDER QUALITY OR PRICE?

When shopping, the price of an item is very important; if money can be saved in one area, it means more can be spent on something else. Supermarkets and high street stores seem to be continually having sales or offering goods at discounted prices and some genuine bargains can be found. However, it is sensible to check the details of the product as it could be that the low price is an indication of low quality. The same applies when buying products online, especially as you can only see a picture of the item for sale. The bargain earphones or computer game may turn out to be an inferior copy of the branded product you thought you were buying.

Sometimes buying a cheaper alternative, even if is not such good quality, can be the right decision. For example, a family buying a kettle and toaster for their caravan might be happy to spend a lot less than they would on items for their home. It does not matter if they are not high quality products as they will be used only occasionally.

www.shoparound.org.uk
This local website has interactive activities about knowing your rights as a consumer.

IS IT BETTER TO BUY OR RENT?

This is a very important consideration, especially when it comes to housing. As property is so expensive, most people are not in a position to be able to pay cash for a house or flat. There are two main alternatives_ either to buy through a mortgage or to rent. A mortgage works in the same way as a loan. The money to buy the property is lent to the buyer by a bank or building society, and this has to be paid back with interest. As the sum of money involved will usually be very large, a mortgage can take up to twenty-five years or longer to pay back.

There are many different types of mortgage available, aimed at meeting the different needs of home buyers.

For example:
Repayment Mortgage – Each month a small proportion of the loan is paid back, with interest.

Interest Only Mortgage – The monthly repayments only go towards paying the interest charges and not the loan itself. An investment plan is taken out alongside the mortgage, to mature at the end of the mortgage. When an investment matures it means a sum of money is paid out at the end of the investment period. This lump sum is then used to pay off the mortgage.

BUYING YOUR HOME

Advantages:

– If a person pays a mortgage then at the end of the period of the loan they will own their property.
– Buying property is often considered to be a good investment as house prices usually increase over time.
– Being a home owner can help to improve a person's credit rating.
– If you own your home, you can do what you like with it. Any alterations or improvements are up to you.

Disadvantages:

– Buying your own home can be a very expensive option; any repairs and maintenance are the responsibility of the home owner.
– The monthly mortgage payments may vary depending on the rate of inflation. Repayments that seemed manageable when taking out the mortgage can spiral out of control if interest rates rise.
– There are no guarantees with property prices and the market could crash at any time. This means a person could be paying far more for their home than it is worth. If they decide to sell and move house, then they will lose even more money.
– A mortgage is a secured loan. This means that if a buyer cannot keep up with the repayments, the bank or building society has the right to sell the house to get their money back.

Taking out a mortgage is a huge financial commitment and many people feel that renting their home is best for them.

RENTING YOUR HOME

Advantages:

– A person might have such a poor credit history that they cannot get a mortgage and renting is the only option open to them.

– The initial costs of renting are much lower than with a mortgage, especially if the house or flat is already furnished. There are no solicitor's fees when taking out a rent agreement as there are with a mortgage.
– Renting gives more flexibility as it is much quicker and easier to move somewhere else. It is necessary to give the landlord notice, perhaps a month, but selling a house can take months or even years.
– The landlord is responsible for any repairs and maintenance.

Disadvantages:

– There is not usually the same feeling of security with a rented property. Tenants do have rights against eviction, but if a tenancy contract expires and is not renewed, the person will have to leave the property.

– The money paid in rent is not going towards something you are buying for yourself, as with a mortgage.
– Some tenants may have to share part of the property with other people and this could lead to conflict.
– The landlord may decide to economise when it comes to maintaining and repairing the property, and this could lower the quality of a person's home. Also, you may not be allowed to redecorate according to your own taste.

A person's circumstances will determine whether renting or buying is the best option. A younger person with few family commitments may appreciate the freedom that comes with renting a property. However, as people get older and become more settled, perhaps with a family, then buying a home is often their first choice.

SHOULD I BUY NEW OR SECOND HAND?

Sometimes buying second hand is a great way to get a bargain. Charity shops are booming and many people are happy to buy nearly-new items at a fraction of their original cost. Buying second hand online is also becoming increasingly popular and is now seen as an acceptable alternative to buying new items in a shop.

If you have to buy something expensive that you will not need very often – a rucksack, perhaps, for a one-off trip – then a cheaper second hand one might be best. You might decide to take up a new sport or learn to play a musical instrument. Starting out with second hand equipment would be cheaper and you could buy new later on if you enjoy the activity.

Some careful considerations need to be made before buying second hand:

- Did the item originally have a guarantee? Can I be reasonably certain that it is not going to break or develop a fault? These are important questions if buying an electrical item.

- The item may appear to be in good condition, but is there any way of telling if it has had heavy use?

- Do you know and trust the person you are buying from? A second hand crash helmet might seem a bargain, but not if it has been in an accident and will give you only limited protection.

ACTIVITY

Consider the following example:

> *Patrick is 24 years old, single, and earns a decent wage as a sales rep. He wants to buy a car and needs something reliable as he will be using it for work as well as leisure activities. Patrick has £5,000 in a savings account. However, he cannot decide whether to spend this money on a second hand car or borrow more money so he can buy something new.*

- Use the Internet to research the advantages and disadvantages of buying a new car rather than a second hand one.

- What advice would you give to Patrick in his situation?

GETTING INTO DEBT

A person who is in debt owes money to someone. Being in debt is becoming part of modern life. Many people owe money, for example, a house mortgage or a loan taken to help buy a car. As long as the repayments can be met, then there is usually no problem.

However, owing money that you cannot afford to pay back is a very bad situation to be in. As bills and repayments spiral out of control, there is the temptation to borrow even more money to make ends meet. A person in this situation can be particularly vulnerable to the loan companies who advertise their 'instant solutions' to debt, which can lead to even more problems.

The term **'loan shark'** refers to an unscrupulous money lender who offers an unsecured loan at a high rate of interest, usually to someone who is desperate and has no other alternative. A borrower who is unable to meet the repayments may be threatened with violence or blackmail, so there is the pressure to borrow even more money. The aim of a loan shark is to keep their customers trapped by debt, so they constantly have to make repayments. Loan sharks are often associated with criminal activities.

REASONS FOR DEBT

Here are some reasons why a person may end up in debt:

Poor budgeting – One of the benefits of having a budget, and keeping to it, is that it gives someone an overview of their spending as a whole. This means it is easier to see where over-spending occurs and whether a reduction can be made. With poor budgeting, one financial set-back, such as an expensive car repair, can lead someone to borrow money and get into debt.

Redundancy – People become used to a certain standard of living based on their earnings. If a person loses their job then spending will have to be reduced, but in the meantime bills still have to be paid and this can lead to debt. For example, a person may not be able to pay their mortgage if they become unemployed, but moving to a cheaper property takes time.

Business failure – A person who is self-employed could be in a very bleak situation if their business collapses. They will face difficulties with household expenses but may also end up in debt to their business customers.

Poor health – A person who cannot work or earn a regular wage through ill health could find themselves in debt. The problem may be even worse if they have taken out a loan to pay for private medical treatment.

Breakdown in a relationship – If a married couple decide to separate or divorce, then any property they were buying together may have to be sold. The house contents will then have to be divided between them. Both adults in the broken relationship may struggle to make ends meet, particularly the parent who has responsibility for the children.

Increase in family size – Babies and children can be very expensive and an addition to the family could cause financial problems. It is necessary to sort out priorities and budget very carefully to avoid debt.

Addiction problem – A person who is an addict will be compelled to feed their addiction, rather than make sensible choices about money. Even if there is a family to consider, they will be unable to put their needs first. In a situation like this, it would be difficult for a family to stay out of debt, especially if it is one of the wage-earners who has the problem. A person who is addicted to gambling would have a very high risk of getting into debt. A compulsive gambler might risk huge sums of money on the outcome of a horse race or game of cards, always hoping for the big win that will get them out of debt. The reality is that gambling is one of the fastest ways to get into debt!

Debt can be caused by a variety of reasons, sometimes poor choices, personal problems or irresponsibility with money. However, many hard working, responsible people find themselves in debt through no fault of their own; they are simply a victim of circumstances.

THE CONSEQUENCES OF DEBT

Being in debt might lead to the following problems:

More debt – The person whose debts are out of control may be tempted to borrow more money to pay existing debts. Accumulating more debt is likely to make the situation worse, especially if the person in debt has to borrow from a loan shark.

Legal problems – A person could be taken to court for non-payment of debts, particularly if these debts are associated with a business. Even if a person does not end up in court, a history of debt can affect their credit rating, making it difficult to borrow money in the future.

Loss of property – If the payments on a mortgage or secured loan are not made, then a person may lose their home. If a person is in debt but does not own their home, then the courts can authorise bailiffs to remove any valuable possessions from their property. Bailiffs are hired by the organisations who lend money and the items they take will be sold to repay debts.

Social problems – There can be social stigma attached to being in debt if a person has to move to a cheaper house or give up a luxurious lifestyle.

Health problems – Being in debt can cause enormous stress and have an effect on mental health. A person who is worried about their financial situation can experience feelings of inadequacy and despair about the future. Constant worry can also have an impact on a person's physical health and well-being.

Relationship problems – Debt, and all the problems associated with it, can put an intolerable strain on relationships. A husband or wife may feel angry and disappointed with their partner, perhaps blaming them for the family's financial problems. They may resent having to change their lifestyle through what they consider to be their partner's lack of judgement or poor financial decisions.

HOW TO COPE WITH DEBT

The following strategies may be useful for a person who is in debt:

Keep to a budget – It is important for a person who is facing problems with debt to get an overview of their financial situation. This will involve keeping track of all expenses and working out a realistic budget to try and reduce spending.

Talk to creditors – It may be possible to re-negotiate the terms of a loan, mortgage or credit agreement. A reputable money lender, such as a bank or building society, would rather have a loan repaid than have to re-possess a property or force a person into bankruptcy.

Prioritise debts – Some debts will be more important than others, for example, paying the mortgage or electricity bill. These should be cleared first.

Avoid borrowing more money – A possible exception to this might be if a person was to borrow money from family or friends, interest free, to help them through a particularly difficult situation. The money still has to be paid back, but a family member might be flexible and understanding about repayments.

Use cash not cards – With cash, a person can only spend what they have – unlike credit cards. Paying credit card bills should be a priority as late payment fees and interest rates can work out to be very expensive.

Debt consolidation – This involves merging a number of loans together into one manageable repayment. This new loan will probably be paid back over a longer period of time than the original debts, to keep the repayments lower. However, this option is usually considered to be a last resort. A debt consolidation company will charge a fee for taking over a person's existing loans and the interest rate on the new loan may be higher than on the original debts.

Take some advice – The Citizen's Advice Bureau offers free, independent advice on a wide range of financial and legal issues. It is a registered charity and unlike a loan company, it will not advise a person to take on more and more debt!

evaluation

Evaluate some of the reasons why a person may get into debt.

HOW TO BE 'MONEY SMART'

Some tips to help you be smart with money…

- Make a budget – and stick to it.
- Make sure you know the difference between a 'need' and a 'want'.
- Cut down on non-essential spending.
- Shop around and make sure you are getting the best price.
- Save money – use a savings account and try to earn some interest.
- Be smart about advertising and only buy something because you want to.
- Only spend what you have – do not borrow from your friends unless it is an emergency.

Can you think of any other tips? Discuss in small groups and come up with helpful tips for the rest of the class.

CHECK YOUR LEARNING

- Give an example of a situation where it might be best to buy:
  - an item that is cheap, but not very high quality
  - a more expensive item that is better quality
  - something that is new and comes with a guarantee
  - a second hand item
  - online
  - in a shop
- Write a paragraph to explain how being in debt could have a negative impact on the whole family.

EXAM FOCUS

The exam skills we have focussed on are sometimes called Assessment Objectives. So far, we have covered:

AO1 – demonstrating your knowledge and understanding

AO2 – applying your knowledge and understanding

The final skill to practice is AO3 – Showing the ability to investigate, analyse and evaluate information.

Questions testing AO3 usually require a longer answer. To gain high marks you will need to write clearly, organise your material and develop your ideas. Your answer will be based partly on your own knowledge and partly on a short article you will be given to read.

The following question tests this skill:

With reference to the extract below and your own knowledge, assess how a person in debt could be helped. [10 marks]

> The number of people getting into debt in Northern Ireland is on the increase, a finance advice agency has said.
>
> Advice NI said thousands of families and individuals were facing greater difficulties in dealing with their finances in the aftermath of Christmas. The group is launching a training programme to provide the "best possible advice" on money and debt issues. The programme is aimed at voluntary advice groups, credit unions, student and public and private sector bodies. Advice NI director Bob Stronge said people all too often found themselves in debt and felt they had no one to turn to. "They can often feel isolated and ashamed and even severely depressed or suicidal," he said. "Local advice agencies are there to help and through this unique programme Advice NI will offer advisors the blend of skills and expertise to do so effectively."
>
> Story from BBC NEWS: 2007
> Source: http://news.bbc.co.uk/go/pr/fr/-/1/hi/northern_ireland/6277199.stm

GLOSSARY

ABORTION: An operation to remove the foetus from the womb.

ABSTINENCE: Making a positive decision not to do something, for example, drink alcohol.

ADOPTION: A couple (or single person) is legally given care of a child to raise as their own, on a permanent basis.

ANNUAL PERCENTAGE RATE (APR): The rate at which interest is charged on a loan.

ANOREXIA: An eating disorder where sufferers follow a strict diet, sometimes to the point of starvation.

BALANCED DIET: A diet with the correct proportions of nutrients and food types to maintain good health.

BLENDED FAMILY: A family following a re-marriage where there may be children from the new relationship, with the addition of older children from previous marriages.

BODY MASS INDEX (BMI): A calculation that can be used to measure levels of obesity.

BUDGET: A balance between expenses and the money that is available to spend.

BULIMIA: An eating disorder where a sufferer will make themselves sick, or abuse laxatives, in an attempt to control their weight.

CREDIT CARD: A card which allows money to be borrowed in order to pay for goods and services.

CREDIT LIMIT: The maximum amount a person is allowed to borrow on a credit card or store card.

CREDIT RATING: A record held in a database of whether a person has not met repayments on a previous loan.

DEBIT CARD: A card which gives direct access to a person's account; money is debited electronically when goods and services are paid for.

DEPRESSANT DRUG: A chemical which causes the body's reactions to slow down.

DIRECT DEBIT: A method of paying bills, where money is taken on a regular basis from a person's account.

DYSCALCULIA: A learning difficulty which can cause problems with numbers.

DYSLEXIA: A learning difficulty which can cause problems with reading and spelling.

EXTENDED FAMILY: A family where there are more than two generations living together, for example, parents, children and grandparents.

FOSTER FAMILY: A family caring for a child on a temporary basis.

HALLUCINOGENIC DRUG: A chemical substance which causes the user to experience hallucinations; sometimes these can be very unpleasant.

HEALTH TRIANGLE: The combination of being in good health, physically, emotionally and socially.

INTEREST ON A LOAN: The amount of extra money that needs to be paid when re-paying a loan.

LOAN SHARK: A money lender who may use violence and blackmail to keep people trapped in debt.

MELANOMA: The most dangerous form of skin cancer, usually caused by too much exposure to the sun.

MORTGAGE: A loan which is taken out over a long period of time and usually used to pay for property.

OBESITY: A medical condition where excess body fat has a negative effect on a person's health.

OPIATE DRUG: A chemical substance which blocks out feelings and makes the user appear cut off from the world.

SELF-CONFIDENCE: A person's own opinion about their talents and abilities.

SELF-ESTEEM: The personal feelings that someone has about themselves.

SELF-WORTH: How a person rates their value in their relationships with other people.

SEXUALLY TRANSMITTED INFECTION (STIs): An infection which is passed on through sexual activity or intimate touching.

SINGLE PARENT FAMILY: A mother or father caring for a child or children without a partner.

STEP-FAMILY: A child's new family following a parent's re-marriage.

STIMULANT DRUG: A chemical which causes the body's functions to speed up.

VEGAN: A person who does not eat (or use) any products from animals.

VEGETARIAN: A person who does not eat meat.

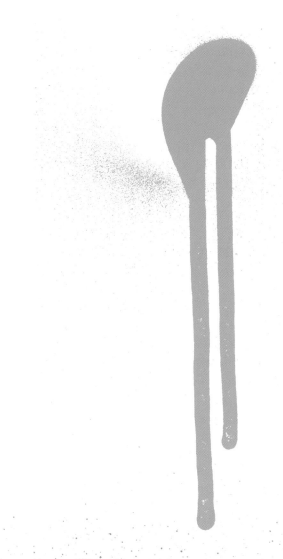

INDEX

ALSO IN THIS SERIES

Presented in the same clear and visually stimulating format as Personal Development, these resources include activities, questions, discussion starters, news items, information files and case studies to encourage active engagement with the topics.

Learning for Life and Work:
LOCAL AND GLOBAL CITIZENSHIP
ISBN: 978-1-906578-71-8

This book follows the specification for unit 3.1, making complex issues accessible and encouraging students to understand their own role as contributors to society.

Learning for Life and Work:
EMPLOYABILITY
ISBN: 978-1-906578-72-5

This book follows the specification for unit 3.3, offering practical advice on the world of work and giving students the opportunity to develop useful skills, personal qualities and attitudes.

Contact Colourpoint Educational at:

Tel: 9182 6339   **Fax:** 9182 1900

Email: sales@colourpoint.co.uk

Web: www.colourpoint.co.uk

Colourpoint Books, Colourpoint House, Jubilee Business Park, 21 Jubilee Road, Newtownards, Co Down, BT23 4YH